LIBRO PRIMO DE LA CROCE

Collegium Musicum, a series of publications of the Department of Music, Yale University, was initiated by the late Leo Schrade in 1955. The continuing aim of the series, as set forth by Professor Schrade in the first volume, is to "present compositions which, through neglect or lack of knowledge, have been ungraciously forgotten or overlooked, despite their artistic value and historical importance." The series is prepared under the general editorship of Leon Plantinga; materials for publication are chosen and editorial policy is established by a committee of the Yale music faculty.

Subscribers to this series, as well as patrons of subscribing institutions, are invited to apply for information about the "Copyright-Sharing Policy" of A-R Editions, Inc., under which the contents of this volume may be reproduced free of charge for performance use.

Correspondence should be addressed to:

A-R Editions, Inc.
315 West Gorham Street
Madison, Wisconsin 53703

COLLEGIUM MUSICUM: YALE UNIVERSITY • SECOND SERIES • VOLUME VIII

LIBRO PRIMO DE LA CROCE

(Rome: Pasoti and Dorico, 1526)

Canzoni, Frottole, and Capitoli

Edited by William F. Prizer

A-R EDITIONS, INC. • MADISON

To
Jim Pruett
and
Howard Smither,
with thanks

ISSN 0147-0108

ISBN 0-89579-101-3

Library of Congress Cataloging in Publication Data:

Main entry under title:

Libro primo de la croce.

(Collegium musicum, second series ; v. 8 ISSN 0147-0108)
For cantus, altus, tenor, and bassus.
1. Frottole. I. Prizer, William F. II. Series.
M2.C64362 vol. 8 [M1579.4] 784'.3064'3 78-4950
ISBN 0-89579-101-3

Contents

Preface

The *frottola* was the principal genre of secular vocal music popular in northern Italy during the period 1480-1530. Unlike the madrigal, whose birthplace was apparently Florence, the *frottola* was cultivated principally in the small courts of northeastern Italy—Ferrara, Padua, Urbino, and, above all, Mantua. The genre was given its greatest impetus through the avid interest of the Marchesa Isabella d'Este Gonzaga who, with her husband Francesco Gonzaga (1466-1519), reigned in Mantua from 1490 until her death in 1539.

The *frottola* may be characterized as a courtly, secular composition intended usually for solo singer and instrumental accompaniment. The texts of the *frottola* were those of the Italian *formes fixes,* the most important being the *barzelletta* and the *strambotto.* The verse itself is most often concerned with love, particularly with its melancholy aspects—love unrequited, betrayed, or occasionally mixed with the pain of parting.[1]

The majority of the composers of the *frottola* were native Italians, in contrast to the *oltremontani* (foreigners from north of the Alps) who were the principal composers of both the sacred and the secular music of Italy during the fifteenth century and, indeed, during the years 1530-1550 immediately following the period when the *frottola* flourished. The most important of these native composers were Marchetto Cara (ca. 1465–1525), Bartolomeo Tromboncino (ca. 1470–after 1535), Michele Pesenti (ca. 1470–ca. 1528), and Filippo de Lurano (ca. 1475–after 1520). The works of these men were included in a large number of manuscripts and prints. Major sources for the earliest period of the *frottola* are the manuscripts Milan, Biblioteca Trivulziana, 55; Modena, Biblioteca Estense, alpha F. 9,9; London, British Museum, Egerton 3051; and Paris, Bibliothèque Nationale, Rés. Vm⁷676.[2]

With the publication of Ottaviano Petrucci's *Frottole Libro primo* (Venice, 1504), prints assumed major importance as sources for the *frottola.* Petrucci himself published thirteen books of *frottole* (eleven for voice and instruments, two for voice and lute) between 1504 and 1514; these prints are the main sources of the *frottola* in this period.

During the years 1510-1520, the principal printer of *frottole* was Andrea Antico of Montona, who worked first in Rome and then in Venice. He published five books of *frottole* for voice and instruments, one book for voice and lute, and another for solo keyboard performance (organ or harpsichord). His prints clearly show an increased interest in the literary quality of the texts, which now include the forms of the madrigal—*canzoni, ballate,* and poetic madrigals.

For the final period of the *frottola,* 1520–1530, the sources are more fragmentary: only seven prints are extant, four of them only in incomplete exemplars.[3] It appears, however, that the center of activity was shifting back to Rome, where Valerio Dorico and Niccolò Judici were the major printers. Of the prints published in the final period, only two contain solely Italian-texted repertory: Petrucci's *Musica di Messer Bernardo Pisano sopra le canzone del Petrarcha,* published in Fossombrone in 1520,[4] and Pasoti and Dorico's *Libro primo de la croce.* The former print consists of a purely Florentine repertory; the latter, though more heterogeneous, represents for the most part composers of northern Italy.

The Print

In April 1526, Jacopo Pasoti and Valerio Dorico of Rome published *Canzoni frottole et capitoli da diversi eccellentissimi musici composti nuovamente stampati et correcti. Libro primo. De la Croce.* The print, published at the expense of the Florentine bookseller Jacopo Giunta, was issued in the oblong choirbook format typical of the *frottola* prints. It was followed in September 1531 by *Canzoni, frottole & capitoli da diversi musici, con novi canzoni agionti composti novamente & stampati. Libro secondo de la croce.* A further edition of *Libro primo de la croce* appeared in January 1533.[5]

All three of these prints appear to be reissues of earlier editions: not only do their titles suggest that they are reprints, but, more conclusively, a *Libro terzo de la croce* was purchased by the Spanish bibliophile Ferdinand Columbus at Rome in 1524.[6] While this third book is no longer extant, its purchase in 1524 must indicate that Books I and II had already been issued by that year. Such a circumstance would help to explain the inclusion of "*capitoli*" in the title of the prints, when no examples of this poetic type are found in the extant editions: one or more *capitoli* could have been included in the first edition of the collection and then could have been deleted from the reprint.[7]

Libro primo de la croce contains twenty-two works, all of which bear ascriptions to composers. These composers range from the principal contributors to the *frottola* repertory (e.g., Marchetto Cara), to those of more peripheral importance (e.g., Francesco Patavino), and to those more closely allied to the style of the early madrigal (e.g., Sebastian Festa). Brief biographies of the composers represented follow in the order of their appearance in the print.

Marchetto Cara (ca. 1465–1525) composed eight works in *Libro primo de la croce.* Cara was born in Verona and was the chief composer at Mantua from 1494 until his death there in late 1525. A favorite of Isabella d'Este and her husband Francesco Gonzaga, Cara served as their *maestro di cappella* from around 1511. He is represented in virtually every collection of *frottole* to appear and is perhaps the most important composer during the final period of the genre.[8]

Sebastian Festa (ca. 1485–1524) is represented by nine or ten works in the print. Festa was born in Villafranca Sabauda near Turin and worked for the Bishop of Mondovì, probably in Rome. Possibly the brother or cousin of Costanzo Festa, he was the composer of at least eleven secular works that are intimately related to the musical style of the early madrigal.[9]

Fra Ruffino Bartolucci (d. after 1539) is responsible for one work in *Libro primo de la croce.* Fra Ruffino was born in Assisi and worked as *maestro di cappella* of the Cathedral in Padua (1510–1520), in Vicenza (1525–1530), and in Assisi (1537–1539). He is the composer of only four secular works within the *frottola* repertory.[10]

Francesco Patavino or Pandulfis (ca. 1497–1556) is the composer of three works in the print. Also known as Francesco Santacroce, Patavino is the most probable composer of the works in *Libro primo de la croce* ascribed to "F. P.," although Gaetano Cesari has suggested Fra Pietro da Hostia as a possible composer.[11] Francesco was born in Santa Croce, a suburb of Padua, and worked as a singer at the Cathedral of that city and as *maestro di cappella* in Treviso, Chioggia, Udine, and Loreto. He is the composer of seven secular works, including those in *Libro primo de la croce.*[12]

Bartolomeo Tromboncino (ca. 1470–after 1535) possibly composed one work in the print. Tromboncino, like Cara, was born in Verona and worked the earlier part of his life (ca. 1489–1501) at Mantua. After leaving the Mantuan court, he went to Ferrara and then to Venice, where he applied for citizenship and a composer's patent in 1521. He was still living in Venetian territory in 1535. Tromboncino was the most productive frottolist and is important for his early interest in the more elegant, madrigal-like text forms. He played little part, however, in the development of the genre after 1520. Only one composition is ascribed to him in *Libro primo de la croce.* This work, *Non al suo amante* (No. [8]), is ascribed to Tromboncino on f. 12v, but to Cara on f. 13r and f. 13v.[13] The present editor feels, however, that the work was more likely composed by Festa, for reasons to be explained below.

The Repertory

The importance of *Libro primo de la croce* lies in its historical position and in the nature of its repertory, for it stands at a crucial point between the late *frottola* and the madrigal; the latter having seen its inception in Florence during the decade 1520–1530. The print is the principal source for the secular works of Sebastian Festa, one of the central figures in the transition from *frottola* to madrigal; it is one of the more important sources for the late works of Marchetto Cara; and it best represents the contradictory, almost paradoxical trends in the *frottola* during its final decade—the tendency toward light works of a "popular" type and the simultaneous tendency toward increasingly elegant madrigal-like texts.

In order to understand these trends, a knowledge of the text forms and style of the *frottola* and early madrigal is necessary. In the discussions of poetic structure that follow, slashes are used throughout to show division of the two halves of symmetrical poetic units. The *frottola* verse of Petrucci's prints is characterized by its extreme regularity; each text form has, within narrow limits, the same number of lines, and each poetic line usually has the same number of syllables. The chief poetic forms of the earlier *frottola* were the *strambotto* and the *barzelletta.* The *strambotto,* a lyric *ottava rima* usually consisting of a single strophe, comprises eight symmetrical lines of eleven syllables each, rhyming ABABABCC.[14] The composer would set this structure in a schematic way: he might write music only for the first pair of lines, in which case the same music would be stated four times; he might add an additional section of music to set the final couplet so that the first section would be stated three times and the last once; or, rarely, he might write new music for each poetic line so that the setting would be through-composed.

The *barzelletta,* by far the most prevalent text form in the period 1500–1510, is a refrain form in which each line is of the same length; the usual length is eight syllables, although seven-syllable lines are also fairly common. The *barzelletta* is made up of three parts: a four-line *ripresa,* a six- or eight-line stanza, and a refrain, which may be either all or part of the *ripresa* and is sung at the conclusion of each strophe. The stanza itself is divided into two parts—the *piedi* (or *mutazione*) and the *volta,* the latter linking the stanza with the refrain through a return to the initial rhyme. The *volta* comprises two or, less often, four lines. The rhyme scheme of a *barzelletta* is therefore as follows: abba (*ripresa*), cd/cd (*piedi*), da or deea (*volta*), and ab, ba, or abba (refrain).

This poetic structure would then be set by the composer in one of two ways: he might provide music only for the *ripresa* and the refrain, or he might write new music for the stanza. Whichever choice he made, the musical structure would mirror the symmetry of the rhyme scheme. Thus, a *barzelletta* in which only the *ripresa* and refrain are set would have the following form (arabic numerals represent musical phrases; letters indicate the rhyme scheme):

ripresa	*piedi*	*volta*	*refrain*
1 2 3 4	1 2 / 1 2	3 4	1 2
a b b a	c d / c d	d a	a b

A *barzelletta* with new music for the stanza has the following form:

ripresa	*piedi*	*volta*	*refrain*
1 2 3 4	5 6 / 5 6	7 8	1 2
a b b a	c d / c d	d a	a b

Also favored by the frottolists was the sonnet. Although more ambitious than other types of *frottola* poetry in content, the sonnet shares the extreme regularity of line length so characteristic of *frottola* verse. Made up of fourteen eleven-syllable lines, the sonnet comprises two quatrains and two tercets. The composer usually wrote music only for the first quatrain, although settings with new music for the first tercet are also common.[15]

From the publication of Antico's *Canzoni nove* in 1510,[16] *frottola* composers were increasingly interested in the more flexible text forms of the *ballata, canzone,* and the poetic madrigal. These were to be the text forms of the early madrigal, and it is in this matter that the *frottola* was one of the formative influences on the new genre. While the earlier *frottola* verse may be identified by its regularity of line length and rhyme scheme, the verse of the later *frottola* and the early madrigal exhibit more flexible rhyme schemes and line lengths. All of the forms have some alternation between eleven-syllable and seven-syllable lines, and all have a flexible number of lines.[17]

The *ballata*—consisting of a *ripresa, piedi,* and *volta* like the *barzelletta*—is the only one of these new madrigalian forms to contain a refrain. *Ballate* are classified according to the length of their *riprese:* thus, a *ballata minore* has a *ripresa* of two lines; a *ballata mezzana,* three; and a *ballata grande,* four. The *piedi* of a *ballata* may be two couplets, two tercets, or, occasionally, two quatrains. Typically, the *volta* is of three lines, rhyming ddb or eeb, although *volte* of one, two, or four lines are also found.

The *canzone* is considerably freer in structure than the *ballata.* It is divided into two parts—the *fronte* (or *piedi*), and the *sirima.* The number of lines in each section is not constant, but the number of syllables in each line is either seven or eleven. The *fronte* is more tightly structured than the *sirima,* comprising a pair of couplets, tercets, or quatrains, the corresponding lines of which are of the same length (e.g., Ab/Ab, abC/bcA, or AbbC/BaaC). The *sirima* usually begins with a rhyme linking it to the *fronte,* although this is often omitted. The *sirima* itself is simply a succession of rhymed couplets with or without additional interpolated lines; it often ends with a rhymed couplet (e.g., AccDDeFF). Thus the rhyme scheme of Festa's *Vergine sacra* (No. [2]), a *canzone,* is Ab/Ab AccDDeFF.

The poetic madrigal may be divided into two types, both of which were set by composers of the later *frottola* and the early madrigal; these two types are the *Trecento* madrigal and the *Cinquecento* madrigal.[18] The *Trecento* madrigal, typified by the madrigals of Petrarch, is usually made up of two tercets followed by a *ritornello* of two lines. The rhyme scheme varies in the tercets, but the lines are usually all of eleven syllables, and the *ritornello* is a rhyming couplet. Thus the rhyme scheme of Festa's setting of Petrarch's *Non al suo amante* (No. [8]) is ABA/BCB CC.

The *Cinquecento* madrigal is a very different type from its namesake of the fourteenth century. Consisting of a free alternation of seven- and eleven-syllable lines, it has no specified rhyme scheme and no specified number of lines. In short, it is the least regular form in the later *frottola* and early madrigal repertory. Fra Ruffin's *Non finsi mai d'amarte* (No. [3]), for example, has the rhyme scheme, aBBCdeeFFGHH.

These distinctions in text forms are important for an understanding of the repertory contained in *Libro primo de la croce.* The contents of this print may be divided into three categories according to text form and musical style: (1) pure *frottole;* (2) works that have more sophisticated, flexible texts and exhibit similarities to the early madrigal; and (3) works incorporating popular texts and tunes.

Works of the first type comprise the smallest repertory in the print: only Cara's *Voi che ascoltate* (No. [1]) and his *Del mio sì grande* (No. [9]) represent pure *frottole.* These two works are typical of the *frottole* published by Petrucci during the first decade of the sixteenth century, but they are not representative of the *frottole* published during the period 1520-1530. They are extremely simple and show none of the forward-looking tendencies, either textual or formal, of the later *frottola.* Indeed, it is possible that both may have been composed at some time considerably earlier than the issue of *Libro primo de la croce.* Both of the texts are already present in the MS Mantua, Biblioteca Comunale A.I.4, a Mantuan collection of *poesia per musica* probably copied before 1510.[19] Since the MS apparently functioned as a repository for the texts of recently composed *frottole,* and since Cara was the principal composer of the Mantuan court, it is possible that the poems in MS A.I.4 represent the texts of Cara's settings. Two additional circumstances strengthen this hypothesis: (1) *Del mio sì grande* (No. [9]) is a *strambotto,* a form little set during the later period of the *frottola;* and (2) the text is by the poet Serafino dall'Aquila, who worked in Mantua during the last decade of the fifteenth century and who died in 1500. Moreover, the text of Cara's *Voi che ascoltate* (No. [1]) had already been set anonymously in Antico's *Canzoni nove* of 1510.[20] Its inclusion in *Libro primo de la croce* may have been due more to the appropriateness of its verse as the opening text in a collection of amorous compositions ("You who hear the sorrowful tears of my former youthful errors, have pity on my sorrow that makes me sigh with such pain") than to its musical interest.

Compositions exhibiting similarities to the early madrigal are more numerous and more representative of Italian secular music of the 1520s than are the pure *frottole* of the first group. This second group consists of twelve pieces, including eight works by Sebastian Festa (Nos. [2], [4], [6], [12], [13], [16], [17], and [20]), Fra Ruffin's *Non finsi mai d'amarte* (No. [3]), Cara's *Piangea la donna mia* (No. [5]), his *Alma gentil* (No. [19]), and the problematic *Non al suo amante* (No. [8], ascribed to both Cara and Tromboncino, but attributed to Festa in the present edition on stylistic grounds which are discussed below).

With regard to text, all twelve are, in fact, madrigals, as they have the typical text forms of the new genre—*ballate, canzoni,* and poetic madrigals. With regard to musical form, they are also madrigals: they are either through-composed or employ occasional structural repetitions.

Until recently, scholars have viewed the madrigal as essentially through-composed; D'Accone, Harrán, and Slim have shown, however, that structural repetitions in the manner of the *frottola* are common in the early madrigal.[21] Philippe Verdelot, shown by Slim to have been among the earliest madrigalists, repeats the music of the *ripresa* in the *volta* of his *Madonna, il tuo bel viso,* a *ballata*-madrigal. In the diagrams below, prime signs following numbers indicate variants of the original melody, letters in parentheses indicate repetitions of the preceding poetic line.[22]

ripresa	*piedi*	*volta*
1 2 3	4 5 6 / 7 8 9	1 2 3 3′
a B B	C d E / C d E	e F F (F)

More striking yet is Verdelot's setting of *Qual maraviglia, o donna,* a *ballata mezzana:*[23]

ripresa	*piedi*	*volta*
1 2 2′	3 4 / 3 4	1′ 1′ 5
a b b	c d / c d	b b (b)

Here, not only do the *ripresa* and the *volta* share the same music, but also the *piedi* are set in the traditional symmetrical fashion of the *barzelletta.*

Within *Libro primo de la croce,* five of Festa's compositions are essentially through-composed (Nos. [2], [12], [16], [17], and [20]), whereas three (Nos. [4], [6], and [13]) show a greater amount of repetition. *Perchè quel che mi trasse* (No. [6]), for example, employs structural repetition in the *piedi:*

ripresa	*piedi*	*volta*
1 2 3	4 5 / 4 5	6 2′ 7
A b B	C d / C d	D b B

Even more concise is Cara's *Piangea la donna mia* (No. [5]). In it, the composer not only treats the *piedi* in the same manner as did Festa in *Perchè quel che mi trasse,* but he also sets the *volta* with the music of the *ripresa.* While this tripartite scheme was the traditional method of setting a *ballata,*[24] it is also found in the early madrigal.[25] A schematic representation of Cara's *ballata* follows:

ripresa	*piedi*	*volta*
1 2 3	4 5 6 / 4 5 6	1 2 3 7 8
a a B	c D E / d E C	e e B (B) (B)

More interesting is Cara's *Alma gentil* (No. [19]). Cara treats this poem (again a *ballata mezzana*) in a completely through-composed manner:

ripresa	*piedi*	*volta*
1 2 3	4 5 6 7 / 8 9 10 11	12 13 14
A B B	C D e E / C D c E	E B B

This choice of a through-composed structure is typical of Cara's later works; of his thirteen compositions that have madrigal-like text forms, nine are essentially through-composed.[26] This previously unrealized trait of through-composition in Cara's late compositions gives added importance to his works as immediate forerunners of the madrigal; in both text and form, they are identical with the early madrigal.

The same may not be said, however, of the texture of Cara's late works. His compositions with madrigal-like texts contain inner voices that are more active rhythmically than the outer voices, often having a greater range and eliding interior cadences. Characteristic of the early madrigal, on the other hand, is a texture in which all parts are vocally conceived and relatively smooth; the inner voices either move in a homophonic fashion with the outer voices or participate in imitation with them. In contrast, the inner voices of Cara's late works tend to be even more active rhythmically than in his earlier works, thus showing no trend toward the texture of the early madrigal.

The compositions of Festa and Fra Ruffin are closer to the early madrigal in texture. These works usually move in homorhythmic semibreves and minims, contain a high percentage of simultaneous cadences, and often have phrases separated by rests in all voices. Three of Festa's works, *Vergine sacra* (No. [2]), *Se 'l pensier che mi strugge* (No. [13]), and *Ben mi credea passar* (No. [16]), also include some imitation.

These observations concerning texture may also be applied to the problematic *Non al suo amante* (No. [8]). This work is almost exclusively homorhythmic and contains only one elided cadence (m. 25). After each of the other interior cadences, the composer has included a simultaneous rest of either a minim or a semibreve, and the inner voices contain few of the wide leaps characteristic of the inner voices of the *frottola*. The style of *Non al suo amante* resembles, therefore, none of the late works of Cara or Tromboncino, all of which maintain the active and angular inner voices of the *frottola*. It is, however, perfectly consistent with the style of Sebastian Festa, as exemplified in his works in *Libro primo de la croce*. Moreover, *Non al suo amante* is included anonymously in the MS Bologna, Civico Museo Q 21, where it is followed immediately by Festa's *Amor, se voi ch'io torni*. That manuscript, of Florentine provenance, contains at least six other works attributable to Festa, but none attributable to either Tromboncino or Cara.[27] It seems likely, therefore, that one should remove *Non al suo amante* from the *opera* of Tromboncino and Cara and attribute it to Sebastian Festa on a tentative basis.

The final category of pieces in *Libro primo de la croce* comprises those works that include popular texts and tunes. These compositions may be subdivided into two smaller groups—those that use the tune within a *frottola*-like framework and those that may be classified as true *villotte*.

The only representative of the former type is Cara's *Poichè in van* (No. [10]). Here the composer has incorporated the popular tune *Vegnando da Bologna* in the *ripresa* of a *barzelletta*. Like many *barzellette* using popular elements, Cara's work is inverted poetically so that the stanza precedes the *ripresa*. In this way, the composer could mock the usual text of the *frottola* by having a stanza that expresses the typical amorous sentiments, immediately followed by the nonsensical popular text—in this instance, "Coming from Bologna, my shoes hurt my feet."

This kind of work, however, was by no means new in *Libro primo de la croce*. Already in Petrucci's third book of *frottole* (Venice, 1505), Tromboncino is represented by the *barzelletta Poichè volse la mia stella*, which contains the popular melody *Che fa la ramacina* ("What are you doing, my little twig?") in the inverted *ripresa*.[28]

More numerous and more representative of the lighter works of the 1520s are the seven *villotte* contained in *Libro primo de la croce* (Nos. [7], [11], [14], [15], [18], [21], and [22]). The *villotta* may be characterized as a polyphonic setting of a popular tune and text. The tune is used throughout the composition, and the text is often in dialect. The *villotta* may include a *nio*, a dance-like refrain, and a *lilolela*, a series of nonsense syllables immediately preceding the *nio*. In contrast to the true *frottola*, which is a *cantus*-dominated solo song, the *villotta* seems to have been intended for voices on all parts: the tenor often begins alone, no one voice includes the entire text, and dialogues between voices or pairs of voices are frequently present.

These *viollotte* may be divided into two types, one which carries a single popular tune in the tenor, and another—the *incatenatura*—which is a true quodlibet containing snippets of many popular tunes. *Libro primo de la croce* includes only two such quodlibets—*Un cavalier de Spagna* (No. [11]) and *Vrai dieu d'amor* (No. [15]), both by Francesco Patavino.[29]

The accompanying table shows the text form and musical type of each work in *Libro primo de la croce.*

Performance[30]

The manner of performance of a work from *Libro primo de la croce* is intimately related to the stylistic group to which the work belongs. For the *frottole* (Nos. [1] and [9]) and for the *frottola*-like

The Repertory of *Libro primo de la croce*

No.	Incipit	Composer	Text Form (Poet)	Type*
[1.]	Voi che ascoltate	M. Cara	Sonnet	I
[2.]	Vergine sacra	S. Festa	Canzone	IIIa
[3.]	Non finsi mai d'amarte	Fra Ruffino Bartolucci	Madrigal	IIIa
[4.]	O passi sparsi	S. Festa	Sonnet (Petrarch)	IIIa
[5.]	Piangea la donna mia	M. Cara	Ballata mezzana	IIIb
[6.]	Perchè quel che mi trasse	S. Festa	Ballata mezzana (Petrarch)	IIIa
[7.]	Dillà da l'acqua sta	F. Patavino	Villotta	IIb
[8.]	Non al suo amante	Tromboncino or Cara (attributed to Festa in the present edition)	Madrigal (Petrarch)	IIIa
[9.]	Del mio sì grande	M. Cara	Strambotto (S. dall'Aquila)	I
[10.]	Poichè in van	M. Cara	Barzelletta	IIa
[11.]	Un cavalier de Spagna	F. Patavino	Villotta	IIb
[12.]	Amor, se voi ch'io torni	S. Festa	Canzone (Petrarch)	IIIa
[13.]	Se 'l pensier che mi strugge	S. Festa	Canzone (Petrarch)	IIIa
[14.]	Le son tre fantinelle	M. Cara	Villotta	IIb
[15.]	Vrai dieu d'amor	F. Patavino	Villotta	IIb
[16.]	Ben mi credea passar	S. Festa	Canzone (Petrarch)	IIIa
[17.]	Come senza costei viver	S. Festa	Canzone (Dertonese)	IIIa
[18.]	E discalza e discalzetta	M. Cara	Villotta	IIb
[19.]	Alma gentil, che di tua vaga spoglia	M. Cara	Ballata mezzana	IIIb
[20.]	Amor, che me tormenti	S. Festa	Ballata-madrigal	IIIa
[21.]	L'ultimo dì de maggio	S. Festa	Villotta	IIb
[22.]	E dapoi che 'l sol dal monte	M. Cara	Villotta	IIb

*Sigla for stylistic types:

I = *Frottola*

II = Popular-based composition
IIa = *Frottola* with popular tune in *ripresa*
IIb = *Villotta*

III = Madrigal-like composition
IIIa = Madrigal-like in text form, musical structure, and texture
IIIb = Madrigal-like in text form and musical structure only

Poichè in van (No. [10]), a performance by solo voice accompanied by instruments on the lower parts appears to have been the most common. Cara's works with madrigal-like texts (Nos. [5] and [19]) also would be rendered best with instruments alone on the *altus, tenor,* and *bassus* parts. These instruments might be melody instruments such as viols, flutes, or recorders, or all of the lower voices might be combined on the harpsichord, organ, or lute. If lute is chosen, it would be permissible to omit the *altus* as was done in contemporaneous lute intabulations. Indeed, any of the compositions could be performed with instruments alone on the lower voices except the *villotte,* which often have portions of their text only in these parts.

All of the *villotte* (Nos. [7], [11], [14], [15], [18], [21], and [22]) would be better rendered with voices on all parts, as would the madrigal-like compositions of Sebastian Festa and Fra Ruffino. Instruments may be used, however, to double the vocal lines. A strictly instrumental performance is also possible.

For most of the compositions in *Libro primo de la croce,* the question of repeats is not problematic. In general, all repeats are to be followed whenever present in the edition. Three of the works, however, present special problems, and specific indications for the performance of these works follow.

Voi che ascoltate (No. [1]) is a sonnet, comprising two quatrains and two tercets. In order to perform the entire text, the setting must be sung four times, twice with the repeated strain (mm. 5–8) for the quatrains and twice without for the tercets. The resulting scheme is as follows:

first quatrain—			*second quatrain—*			*first tercet—*			*second tercet—*		
1	‖: 2 :‖	3	1	‖: 2 :‖	3	1	2	3	1	2	3
A	B	A	A	B	A	C	D	C	C	D	C
	B			B							

Del mio sì grande (No. [9]) is a *strambotto* in which only the first couplet is set. The musical setting must be repeated for each of the remaining couplets.

Poichè in van (No. [10]) is a *barzelletta* in which the stanza precedes the *ripresa.* It has an incomplete text, the first stanza lacking a pair of lines. The repetition sign should be ignored in the performance of the first stanza, but should be followed for the second stanza, which is complete.

Finally, a word concerning changes of meter may be helpful to the performer. Eleven of the works in the present edition, all in C or ₵, have measures of three half-notes inserted. In such cases, the time signature is placed in brackets and does not change the basic pulse. These measures of three half-notes have been inserted by the editor so that major sections of works or entire pieces may conclude with a full measure.

Three of the works, however, include changes of meter in the original. Both *Poichè in van* (No. [10]) and *Un cavalier de Spagna* (No. [11]) include sections marked "3" in the print. This "3" indicates *proportio tripla,* and the following sections should be performed so that the dotted half-note equals the half-note of the preceding section (𝅗𝅥 = 𝅗𝅥.).[31] *Vrai dieu d'amor* (No. [15]) begins in *tempus imperfectum diminutum* (₵) and concludes with a section in simple *tempus imperfectum* (C). This change should indicate an augmentation, in which the half-note in ₵ equals the quarter-note in C (𝅗𝅥 = ♩). It is possible, however, that the equivalence intended is not exact, but rather indicates simply a slight slowing of the *tactus.*

Editorial Procedures

In the transcriptions that follow, the scoring of the works has followed the readings given in Pasoti and Dorico's *Libro primo de la croce* and no attempt has been made to create a composite "ideal version" from all sources that contain a given work. The sources of each composition have been collated, but variants present in them have been accepted only if the primary source is obviously in error. Major differences have been recorded in the notes, but minor discrepancies such as simple rhythmic differences or differences in orthography have not been recorded.

One exception to the above rule must be noted. Although the lower voices are given only textual incipits in Pasoti and Dorico's print, the full texts have been added in three instances:

(1.) Texts are added to the lower parts if concordant sources contain texts for all voices. In cases in which a division of a note-value is necessary as a result of including the text, the original value is recorded in the Critical Notes. Texts are not added in the lower voices to Cara's *Piangea la donna mia* (No. [5]) nor to his *Alma gentil* (No. [19]), even though both are texted throughout in Vnm 1795. The active inner voices of these compositions are typical of the instrumental lines of the *frottola.* Attempts to add text to these voices meet with little success, and it is clear that they were intended as instrumental parts.

(2.) Texts are added to the lower voices of pieces in the style of works included in other sources with full texts. Thus, Sebastian Festa's *Vergine sacra* (No. [2]) and *Perchè quel che mi trasse* (No. [6]) are included here with full texts, even though both are *unica.* Their style is fully consistent with Festa's madrigals that are texted in other sources.

(3.) Texts are added to *villotte* in which texted lower voices are necessary. In many of the *villotte* there are dialogues between upper and lower voices in which the cantus does not include the full text; in others the tenor begins alone and the textual incipits of the other voices begin with a later portion of the text. These pieces have also been provided with full texts.

While the procedure of texting the lower voices is not in harmony with the practice found in the print, it allows the performers to sing all voices if they so desire. All editorial additions of text have been italicized. In some instances, small portions of the text were included in the lower voices in the print. Such instances occur either at page-turns, where a new incipit is given (e.g., No. [2], mm. 39-40), or in *villotte* that include short dialogues (e.g., No. [7], mm. 14-17). These texts are left in roman type.

Orthography has generally been left as it was in the print; only when the meaning or pronunciation of a word requires an additional letter has the orthography been changed (e.g., in No. [13], m. 24, "giaccio" has been changed to "g*h*iaccio"). In such cases, the single letters are italicized.

In the transcriptions, the original note values have been halved, and the final notes of each piece have been represented by whole-notes with *fermate,* whether a long or a breve was notated in the print. Only modern clefs have been used, but incipits at the beginning of each piece show the original clefs, signatures, mensuration signs, and nomenclature of voices.

Bar lines have been added according to modern practice, and, insofar as possible, the barring has been kept regular throughout. Often a measure of three halves (three semibreves in the original) instead of two halves was necessary to allow the composition to conclude with a full measure. In such cases, the time signatures have been placed in brackets.

The *stanghette* (heavy vertical lines) of the print have been rendered in two different ways, depending on their function. Where they mark the end of major sections, double bars have been used; where they form the beginning of repeated sections, modern repetition signs have been used.

Ligatures are indicated by a solid bracket (┌───┐), and coloration by an open bracket (┌─ ─┐). *Minor color* has been represented by a dotted quarter and an eighth rather than a triplet.

Editorial accidentals, affecting only the note over which they fall, have been added sparingly according to the following precepts: (1.) at cadence points the seventh degree has been raised if such an alteration does not cause an harmonic tritone or a simultaneous cross-relation; (2.) accidentals have been added to avoid both melodic and harmonic tritones and simultaneous cross-relations; (3.) flats have been added to b and e in accordance with the maxim, "Una nota super la semper est canendum fa"; (4.) when necessary, thirds contained in final cadences and in important medial cadences have been raised to make the third major.

Sources

A. Prints

RISM 1526[6]	*Canzoni frottole et capitoli da diversi eccellentissimi musici composti nuovamente stampati et correcti. Libro primo. De la Croce.* Rome: Pasoti and Dorico, 1526.
RISM [1531][3] [*recte* 1533]	*Canzoni frottole et capitoli da diversi eccellentissimi musici con novi canzoni agionti & composti novamente & stampati. Libro primo de la Croce.* Rome: Dorico, 1533.
RISM [ca. 1520][7]	*Frottole de Misser Bartolomio Tromboncino et de Misser Marcheto Carra con tenori et bassi tabulati et con soprano in canto figurato per cantar et sonar col lauto.* [Venice: Andrea Antico, 1520.]

B. Manuscripts

Bc 21	Bologna, Civico Museo Bibliografico Musicale, MS Q 21.
Fc 2440	Florence, Biblioteca del Conservatorio di Musica, MS Basevi 2440.
Fn 111	Florence, Biblioteca Nazionale Centrale, MS Magl. XIX, 111.
Fn 122	Florence, Biblioteca Nazionale Centrale, MS Magl. XIX, 122-125.
Fn 164	Florence, Biblioteca Nazionale Centrale, MS Magl. 164-167.
MAc A.I.4	Mantua, Biblioteca Comunale, MS A.I.4 (texts only).
MOe 11.8	Modena, Biblioteca Estense, MS gamma, L. 11.8.
SGs 463	St. Gall, Stiftsbibliothek, MS 463.
Vnm 1795	Venice, Biblioteca Nazionale Marciana, MS C1. IV, 1795-1798.

Critical Notes

The following paragraphs list concordances and cite divergences among sources as well as enumerate corrections to the print. The abbreviations used are those given in the Sources section of the preface. All comments on rhythm refer to the original values of the sources. In specifying the position of a given note within a measure, a note tied from the preceding measure is regarded as "1." Voice parts are abbreviated as follows: C = cantus, A = altus, T = tenor, and B = bassus. Pitches are designated in the usual manner: c′ is middle C; c″ is one octave above it, and so forth.

[1.] *Voi che ascoltate*—No concordance; text incomplete in print, italicized portion supplied from MAc A.I.4, f. 10v.

Mm. 5-8, C, text for repetition mistakenly placed under mm. 9-12 in print.

[2.] *Vergine sacra*—Concordance: RISM 1531[3] [*recte* 1533] (first half of C and T only).

M. 26, C, A, T, B, notes 4-5, minim in print divided for text-underlay.

[3.] *Non finsi mai d'amarte*—Concordance: MOe 11, 8, f. 23v-24r (contains B, only, anonymous); B texted in MOe 11,8. Revisions: M. 34, A, note 1 is a semiminim in print.

[4.] *O passi sparsi*—Concordances: Bc 21, No. 24 (anonymous); Fn 111, No. 10 (T lacking in source, piece is anonymous); Fn 164, No. 25 (anonymous); MOe 11,8, f. 2v-3r (B only, anonymous). All voices are texted in concordances but second quatrain lacking in Fn 111 and MOe 11,8. *O passi sparsi* is found in sources as late as RISM 1566[22]. Only the sources listed above have been collated.

M. 12, B, note 2 is a in print, Bc 21, Fn 164, and MOe 11,8; the g in this edition follows Fn 111. M. 14, C, 1-2, rhythm is minim (f′) in Bc 21 and Fn 164. M. 20, A, beats 3 and 4, rest omitted and note 2 is a semibreve in Fn 111; M. 27, B, note 1 is a semiminim in print; this edition follows Bc 21, Fn 164, and MOe 11,8. M. 43, B, note 1 is c in print and d in Fn 164 and MOe 11,8; this edition follows Bc 21 and Fn 111. M. 48, T, semibreve-rest lacking in MOe 11,8.

[5.] *Piangea la donna mia*—Concordances: RISM [ca. 1520][7], f. 46v, attributed to M. C. (lute intabulation without A, incomplete); Vnm 1795, No. 85 (anonymous). All voices are texted in Vnm 1795; "riasciugommi" is "raiugommi" and "m'asciuga" is "maisiuga" in print and the revisions here follow Vnm 1795.

M. 8, A, notes 1-3 are semibreve (g), minim (g), minim (f) in Vnm 1795. M. 30, C, note 2 is e′ in Vnm 1795.

[6.] *Perchè quel che mi trasse*—No concordance.

M. 11, C, note 2 has a corona (fermata) above it in print.

[7.] *Dillà da l'acqua sta*—Concordances: SGs 463, No. 151 (C and A only, anonymous); Vnm 1795, No. 95 (anonymous). All voices texted in concordances; text incomplete in print and in SGs 463, and italicized portion supplied from Vnm 1795; "sconta" is "scosta" in print, and revision here follows SGs 463 and Vnm 1795; final strophe lacking in Vnm 1795; final two strophes lacking in SGs 463.

Incipit, C, soprano clef in SGs 463 and Vnm 1795; all parts, mensuration sign C in Vnm 1795. M. 22, B, note 3 is e-flat in Vnm 1795, only, all other sources omit the flat. M. 27, C, note 2 is lacking in SGs 463.

[8.] *Non al suo amante*—Concordance: Bc 21, No. 37 (anonymous). All voices texted in Bc 21, *Non al suo amante* is ascribed to B. T. on f. 12v of *Libro primo de la croce* but to M. C. on f. 13r and 13v. Stylistically, it resembles the works of neither composer and is more probably by Sebastian Festa. See page xi above.

Incipit, T, B, mensuration sign is C in Bc 21 (C, A, mensuration sign is illegible). M. 15, B, note 1 is B in print; this edition follows Bc 21. M. 22, A, note 3 *sic*; note 3 is d′ in Bc 21.

[9.] *Del mio sì grande*—No concordance; text found in MAc A.I.4, f. 63r.

M. 2, A, note 3 is b′ in print.

[10.] *Poichè in van*—No concordance.

M. 13, all parts, mensuration sign 3 in print.

[11.] *Un cavalier de Spagna*—Concordances: Fc 2440, pp. 174-175 (anonymous); Fn 164, No. 43 (anonymous); SGs 463, No. 150 (C, A, only, anonymous); Vnm 1795, No. 96 (anonymous). All voices are texted in Fc 2440, Fn 164, and Vnm 1795; SGs 463 contains only incipits in both voices; final strophe lacking in print and supplied from Vnm 1795.

Incipit, C, soprano clef in SGs 463 and Vnm 1795, mensuration sign is ₵ in Fn 164 and illegible in Fc 2440; A, T, mensuration sign is ₵ in Fc 2440, Fn 164, and Vnm 1795; B, mensuration sign is ₵ in Fc 2440 and Fn 164. M. 5, T, note 4 is a in Vnm 1795. M. 8, A, note 4 is e′ in SGs 463. Mm. 9 and 12, all parts, Fc 2440, Fn 164, SGs 463, and Vnm 1795 have an extra measure after m. 9 and after m. 12. The passage, transcribed from Fn 164, is as shown in Ex. 1 on the following page. M. 17, all parts, mensuration sign is 3. M. 23, all parts, semibreve-rest replaced by breve with a corona and followed by mensuration sign in Fc 2440 and Fn 164; C, A, T, semibreve-rest replaced by breve with a corona and followed

Ex. 1. No. [11], mm. 8-13 as given in Fn 164:

by mensuration sign in Vnm 1795; B, semibreve-rest replaced by breve with a corona lacking mensuration sign.

[12.] *Amor, se voi ch'io torni*—Concordances: Bc 21, No. 38 (anonymous); Fn 164, No. 23 (anonymous). All voices are texted in concordances; "giogo" is "gioco" in print, "pria" is "prima" in print, and the revisions both follow F. Petrarca, *Canzoniere* (Turin, 1975), p. 341.

M. 4, B, notes 2-3, semibreve divided for text-underlay in print; this edition follows Bc 21 and Fn 164. M. 18, A, note 4 is semibreve on d' and Bc 21, and semibreve on e' in Fn 164. Mm. 19-22, C, erroneously marked to be repeated in print, but not in Bc 21 or in Fn 164. M. 32, T, note 1, dotted semibreve divided for text-underlay. M. 37, A, note 1 is g' in Bc 21. M. 41, T, notes 3-4, semibreve divided for text-underlay; this edition follows Bc 21 and Fn 164. Mm. 42–43, B, only four minims on f in print; this edition follows Bc 21 and Fn 164.

[13.] *Se 'l pensier che mi strugge*—Concordance: Bc 21, No. 7 (anonymous). All voices texted in Bc 21.

Incipit, T, alto clef in Bc 21; all parts, mensuration sign C in Bc 21. M. 3, A, notes 1-2, replaced by 4 semiminims on e', d' c', and b in Bc 21; B, note 1 is e-flat in Bc 21. M. 4, A, notes 1-4 are replaced by semibreve on d' in Bc 21. M. 6, A, notes 1-4, replaced by 2 minims on f' and e' in Bc 21. M. 10, C, note 1 is replaced by 4 semiminims on g', f', e', and d' in Bc 21. M. 13, C, change to soprano clef here in print. M. 13, A, note 3 is d' in Bc 21. M. 14, T, notes 3-4 are 2 minims on b-flat in Bc 21. M. 22, A, note 2 is f' in Bc 21. M. 22, T, note 2 is d' in Bc 21. M. 24, A, change to mezzo-soprano clef here in print; note 1 is c' in Bc 21. M. 30, A, rest is replaced by minim (d'), note 1 is e', and note 3 is d' in Bc 21; T, notes 1-3 are 3 minims on a in Bc 21; B, semibreve divided for text underlay; this edition follows Bc 21. M. 32, all parts, Bc 21 has a slightly different and shorter (8-measure) ending from this point:

Ex. 2. No. [13], mm. 32ff, ending as shown in Bc 21:

M. 38, B, notes 1-2, semibreve divided for text-underlay. M. 39, T, change to mezzo-soprano clef here in print. M. 42, B, notes 3-4, semibreve divided for text-underlay.

[14.] *Le son tre fantinelle*—No concordance.

M. 14, T, notes 3-4, semibreve divided for text-underlay. M. 19, note 2 and m. 20, note 1, A, dotted breve divided for text-underlay.

[15.] *Vrai dieu d'amor*—Concordances: Bc 21, No. 46 (anonymous); Fn 122, No. 31 (T lacking, anonymous); MOe 11,8, f. 55v-56r (B only, anonymous). All voices texted in concordances; first line of text is "Vrai diu d'amor chi me confortera" in print, and revision here follows Bc 21 and Fn 122 (this line and several others are attempts of an Italian scribe to spell French). Mm. 19-22 and mm. 26-28, text reads "Ch'io son fora di prison" in Bc 21, Fn 122, and MOe 11,8 and this is closer in sound to the original French; mm. 17-19 and mm. 22-24 read "Falilan falilon," thus rhyming with "prison." Mm. 22 and 23, text reads "O falalalilon" in Bc 21, Fn 122, and

MOe 11,8. M. 33, the word "pino" is lacking in print, and is taken from Bc 21, Fn 122 and MOe 11,8.

Incipit, B, baritone clef in Bc 21. M. 24, A, change to tenor clef here in print; note 2 is e′ in print and Bc 21; note 4 is c′ in print. M. 28, T, note 2, minim-rest replaces this note in print; this edition follows Bc 21. M. 50, B, note 1 is G in Bc 21. M. 51, T, mensuration sign lacking in print, in Bc 21, and Fn 122. M. 51, B, mensuration sign lacking in MOe 11,8.

[16.] *Ben mi credea passar*—Concordances: Bc 21, No. 34 (anonymous); Fn 164, No. 23 (anonymous). All voices are texted in concordances. Mm. 57-65, "è" is "&" (i.e., "e") in print; revision follows Francesco Petrarca, *Canzoniere,* p. 265.

Incipit, C, mensuration sign C in Fn 164. M. 15, A, note 2 is e′ in print; this edition follows Bc 21 and Fn 164. M. 28, C, note 5 is c′ in print, Bc 21 and Fn 164. M. 36, A, notes 1-3, replaced by a semibreve on f in Bc 21. Mm. 65-66, all parts lacking in Bc 21 and Fn 164.

[17.] *Come senza costei viver*—Concordance: Bc 21, No. 40 (anonymous). All voices texted in Bc 21. Another strophe follows at the end of what appears in the present edition in *Opere volgari di M. Luca Valentiano Derthonese* (Venice: Bernardino di Vitalli, 1533 [n.s.]), f. 68r-68v. The rhyme scheme of the first strophe is that of a *ballata mezzana,* but the poem is listed as a *canzone* in the *Opere,* and the rhyme scheme of the second strophe is that of a *canzone.* M. 29, text in print reads "Hai."

M. 4, A, minim-rest replaced by 2 semibreves on a and b in Bc 21. M. 10, T, minim-rest replaced by semibreve on e′ in Bc 21. M. 11, T, note 1 is c′ in print; this edition follows Bc 21. M. 19, A, note 2 is b in Bc 21. M. 24, A, notes 3-4, semibreve divided for text-underlay; this edition follows Bc 21; B, note 3, extra minim (d) in print at this point; this edition follows Bc 21. M. 25, B, notes 1-4, 2 semibreves divided for text-underlay; this edition follows Bc 21. M. 26, note 3, and note 1 of m. 27, all parts, breve divided in all voices for text-underlay. M. 31, C, notes 1-2 are 2 minims on e′ in Bc 21. M. 32, T, notes 1-2, semibreve divided for text-underlay; this edition follows Bc 21; B, notes 3-4, semibreve divided for text-underlay; this edition follows Bc 21. M. 34, T, notes 1-2 replaced by semibreve on d in print; this edition follows Bc 21. M. 35, A, notes 2-3 are 2 semiminims on g in Bc 21. Mm. 40-42, A, T, B, ending differs in Bc 21, as shown in Ex. 3 at the top of the next column.

[18.] *E discalza e discalzetta*—No concordance.

M. 10, A, note 3 and m. 11, note 1, dotted semibreve divided for text-underlay. M. 12, A, notes 1-2, semibreve divided for text-underlay. M. 13, C, T,

Ex. 3. No. [17], mm. 38ff, ending as shown in Bc 21:

note 3 and M. 14, note 1, dotted semibreve divided for text-underlay.

[19.] *Alma gentil, che di tua vaga spoglia*—Concordance: Vnm 1795, No. 78 (anonymous). All voices are texted in Vnm 1795.

M. 8, B, notes 3-4 are 2 minims on G in print; this edition follows Vnm 1795. M. 9, T, notes 1-2 are lacking in print; this edition follows Vnm 1795. M. 12, T, note 4 is c′ in Vnm 1795. M. 19, A, note 4 is d in print; this edition follows Vnm 1795. M. 37, T, note 3 is a in Vnm 1795. M. 45, A, note 3 is c′ in Vnm 1795.

[20]. *Amor, che me tormenti*—Concordances: Bc 21, No. 35 (anonymous); Fn 164, No. 20 (anonymous). All voices are texted in concordances. M. 34, text of print reads "Hai."

M. 8, B, notes 1-2, semibreve divided for text-underlay; this edition follows Bc 21 and Fn 164. M. 11, C, rest lacking in print; this edition follows Bc 21 and Fn 164; A, rest replaced by semibreve (d′) in Bc 21 and Fn 164; B, rest replaced by semibreve (d) in Bc 21 and Fn 164. M. 13, C, notes 1-2, breve divided for text-underlay. M. 18, T, note 1 is e in Bc 21 and Fn 164. M. 30, B, notes 1-2, semibreve divided for text-underlay; this edition follows Bc 21 and Fn 164. M. 33, T, notes 1-2, breve divided for text-underlay; this edition follows Bc 21 and Fn 164. M. 37, C, note 1 is b′ in print; this edition follows Bc 21 and Fn 164. M. 41, C, rest lacking in print; this edition follows Fn 164; entire m. is illegible in Bc 21.

[21.] *L'ultimo dì de maggio*—Concordances: Fc 2440, pp. 176-177 (anonymous); Fn 164, No. 44 (anonymous); Vnm 1795, No. 97 (anonymous). All voices are texted in concordances; final strophe lacking in print, Fc 2440, and Fn 164, and supplied from Vnm 1795.

Incipit, all parts, mensuration sign C in Vnm 1795. M. 3, A, notes 5-6, *sic;* all sources agree; T, notes 3, 4-5, *sic;* all sources agree. M. 9, A, note 3 is e-natural in Fc 2440 and Fn 164. M. 21, T, notes 3-4, semibreve divided for text-underlay; this edition follows Fc 2440, Fn 164, and Vnm 1795. M. 22, T, notes 1-2, semibreve divided for text-underlay; this edition follows Fc 2440, Fn 164, and Vnm 1795. M. 26, C, note 2 is c″ in print; this edition follows Fc 2440, Fn 164, and Vnm 1795. M. 32, T, notes 1-4, 2 semibreves divided for text-underlay; this edition follows Fc 2440, Fn 164, and Vnm 1795. M. 38, T, B, notes 3-4, semibreve divided for text-underlay; this edition follows Fc 2440, Fn 164, and Vnm 1795. M. 40, B, note 1 is F in Fc 2440 and Fn 164.

[22.] *E dapoi che 'l sol dal monte*—No concordance.

M. 8, T, notes 1-2, dotted semibreve divided for text-underlay. M. 10, note 2, and note 1 of m. 11, T, dotted semibreve divided for text-underlay. M. 11, C, note 4 is f′ in print.

Acknowledgments

I should like to thank the Österreichische Nationalbibliothek in Vienna for permission to publish this edition of *Libro primo de la croce* and the various European libraries for allowing me to consult their manuscripts. I should also like to thank Professor Albert Seay, who collated two manuscripts for me, Professor H. Colin Slim, who lent his microfilm of one manuscript, and Signorina Enrica Bragadin for her help with the translation of the texts.

William F. Prizer

October 1977 Villa I Tatti, Florence, Italy

Notes

1. On the style of the *frottola,* see Alfred Einstein, *The Italian Madrigal,* 3 vols. (Princeton, 1949; reprint ed. Princeton, 1971); Walter Rubsamen, *Literary Sources of Secular Music in Italy (ca. 1500)* (Berkeley, 1943; reprint ed. New York, 1972); *idem,* "From Frottola to Madrigal: The Changing Pattern of Secular Italian Vocal Music," *Chanson and Madrigal, 1480-1530,* ed. by James Haar (Cambridge, Massachusetts, 1964), pp. 51-87; and William F. Prizer, "Marchetto Cara and the North Italian Frottola" (Ph.D. diss., University of North Carolina at Chapel Hill, 1974 [Ann Arbor: University Microfilms, Order No. 74-26,927]).

2. Inventories and discussions of all of these MSS are included in Knud Jeppesen, *La Frottola,* vol. 2 (Aarhus, 1969). On Trivulziana 55, see also Remo Giazotto, "Onde musicali nella corrente poetica di Serafino dall'Aquila," *Musurgia Nova* (Milan, 1959), pp. 3-119; and Jeppesen, *La Frottola* (Aarhus, 1970), 3:141-324. On alpha F. 9,9, see Claudio Gallico, "Poesie musicali di Isabella d'Este," *Collectanea historiae musicae* (1963) 3:109-19. On Egerton 3051, see Martin Staehelin, "Eine Florentiner Musik-Handschrift aus der Zeit um 1500 (Quellenkundliche Bemerkungen zur Frottola-Sammlung Ms. Egerton 3051 des British Museum and zum 'Wolffheim-Manuskript' der Library of Congress)," *Schweitzer Beiträge zur Musikwissenschaft,* series 3, vol. 1 (1972): 55-81. On MS 676, see Nanie Bridgman, "Un manuscrit du début du XVIe siècle à la Bibliothèque Nationale (Dep. de la Musique, Rés. Vm.7676)," *Annales musicologiques* (1953) 1:177-267, and (1956) 4:259-60.

3. This figure does not include the 1520 reprints of Antico's third and fourth books of *frottole,* which were first published in 1513 and 1517, respectively. The seven extant prints are inventoried in Jeppesen, *La Frottola* (Aarhus, 1968), I:122, 133, 136-39, and 146. On these collections, see also Jeppesen's "An Unknown Pre-Madrigalian Music Print in Relation to Other Contemporary Italian Sources (1520-1530)," *Studies in Musicology: Essays in the History, Style, and Bibliography of Music in Memory of Glen Haydon,* ed. by James W. Pruett (Chapel Hill, N.C., 1969), pp. 3-17.

4. On Pisano, see Frank A. D'Accone, "Bernardo Pisano, an Introduction to His Life and Works," *Musica Disciplina* (1963) 17:115-35; *idem,* "Bernardo Pisano and the Early Madrigal," *Internationale Gesellschaft für Musikwissenschaft: Report of the Tenth Congress* (Ljubljana, 1967), pp. 96-107; and *idem,* ed., *Music of the Florentine Renaissance,* vol. 1 (American Institute of Musicology, 1966).

5. The 1533 reprint (not 1531 as given in RISM) is extant in a single incomplete exemplar that conserves only the title page, the *tavola,* the dedicatory letter, and the *cantus* and *tenor* of Festa's *Vergine sacra* (No. [2] in the edition of 1526). Both *Libro secondo* and the reprint of *Libro primo* were printed by Dorico alone, without the assistance of Pasoti. For further information on Dorico, see Suzanne G. Cusick, "Valerio Dorico: Music Printer in Sixteenth-century Rome" (Ph.D. diss., University of North Carolina at Chapel Hill, 1975 [Ann Arbor: University Microfilms, Order No. 76-9231]).

6. Catherine Weeks Chapman, "Printed Collections of Polyphonic Music Owned by Ferdinand Columbus," *Journal of the American Musicological Society* 21 (1968): 50.

7. Other explanations for the inculsion of "capitoli" in the title are also possible. Cara's *Voi che ascoltate* (No. [1] in *Libro primo de la croce),* a sonnet, is published with only the first three of its fourteen endecasyllabic lines. These three lines could have been mistaken by the printers for the first stanza of a *capitolo,* a poem consisting of three-line stanzas, all lines of which are also endecasyllabic. It is also possible, however, that the listing of a large number of poetic forms in the title of the print was merely an advertising device, intended to indicate the presence of settings of every type within the collection.

8. For further information on Cara, see William F. Prizer, "Marchetto Cara and the North Italian Frottola," *idem,* "La Capella di Francesco II Gonzaga e la musica sacra a Mantova

nel primo ventennio del Cinquecento," *Atti del Covegno su Mantova e I Gonzaga nella civiltà del Rinascimento* (Verona, 1978), and *idem*, "Marchetto Cara at Mantua: New Documents on the Life and Duties of a Renaissance Court Composer," *Musica Disciplina* 32 (forthcoming, 1978).

9. For further information on Festa, see Jeppesen, *La Frottola*, 1:161-63 and Rubsamen, "Sebastian Festa and the Early Madrigal," *Gesellschaft für Musikforschung: Bericht über den internationalen musikwissenschaftlichen Kongress, Kassel 1962* (Kassel, 1963), pp. 112-26. Nine works are ascribed to Festa in the print; for a possible tenth work by him, see p. xi.

10. For further information on Fra Ruffino, see Jeppesen, *La Frottola*, 1:161.

11. Gaetano Cesari, *Die Entstehung des Madrigals im 16. Jahrhundert* (Cremona, 1908), p. 13. For Patavino as the composer of the works in *Libro primo de la croce*, see Jeppesen, *La Frottola*, 1:66.

12. For further information on Patavino, see Jeppesen, *La Frottola*, 1:155.

13. See plates III and IV for reproductions of f. 12v and 13r. For further information on Tromboncino, see Jeppesen, *La Frottola*, 1:144-52 and Prizer, "Bernardino Piffaro e i pifferi e tromboni di Mantova," *Rivista italiana di musicologia* 13 (forthcoming, 1978).

14. The rhyme schemes here and throughout the preface use capital letters to represent lines of eleven syllables in length and lower-case letters to represent lines of less than eleven syllables.

15. For further discussion of the textual and musical form of the *frottola*, see Nino Pirrotta, "Tradizione orale e tradizione scritta della Musica," *L'Ars Nova italiana del Trecento* (Certaldo, 1970), 3:431-41; and Prizer, "Performance Practices in the Frottola," *Early Music* 3 (1975): 227-35.

16. *Canzoni nove con alcune scelte de varie libri di canto* (Rome: Antico, 1510).

17. The most detailed study on these text forms is Don Harrán, "Verse Types in the Early Madrigal," *Journal of the American Musicological Society* 22 (1969): 25-53. The information on the text forms of the madrigal given here is taken from Harrán's study.

18. Harrán, "Verse Types," pp. 36-41.

19. Gallico, *Un libro di poesie per musica dell'epoca di Isabella d'Este* (Mantua, 1961), pp. 9 and 51-52.

20. F. 14v-15r.

21. See the literature by D'Accone cited in footnote 4 above and his "Transitional Text Forms and Settings in an Early 16th-Century Florentine Manuscript," *Words and Music, the Scholar's View: A Medley of Problems and Solutions Compiled in Honor of A. Tillman Merritt*, ed. by Laurence Berman (Cambridge, Massachusetts, 1972), pp. 29-58. See also Donald Hersh (*alias* Harrán), "Verdelot and the Early Madrigal" (Ph.D. diss., University of California at Berkeley, 1963), pp. 125-84; and H. Colin Slim, *A Gift of Madrigals and Motets* (Chicago, 1972), 1:162-64.

22. *Il primo libro de madrigali di Verdelotto* . . . (Venice: Scotto, 1537 [first published, 1533]), No. 13. Modern edition in Einstein, *The Italian Madrigal*, 3:29-32. A *ballata*-madrigal is a free variant of a *ballata* in which the *volta* does not return to the rhyme of the *ripresa*. On the *ballata*-madrigal, see Harrán, "Verse Types," 33-36.

23. *Il secondo libro de madrigali di Verdelotto* . . . (Venice: Scotto, 1536 [first published, 1534]), No. 21. Modern edition in Prizer, "Marchetto Cara and the North Italian Frottola," 2:285-88.

24. See, for example, the setting of *En bianca vesta* from the MS Bologna, Biblioteca Universitaria 2216, p. 97.

25. Slim, for example, finds two *ballate* and one *ballata*-madrigal which are in a tripartite form in the early Newberry MS (*A Gift of Madrigals and Motets*, 1:162n).

26. See, Prizer, "Marchetto Cara and the North Italian Frottola," 1:206-18.

27. On MS Q 21, see Jeppesen, *La Frottola*, 2:104-107 and Gallico, *Un canzoniere musicale del Cinquecento* (Florence, 1961).

28. *Frottole. Libro tertio* (Venice: Petrucci, 1504 [1505 n.s.]), f. 18v-19r. Modern edition in Einstein, *The Italian Madrigal*, 3:75-76. A modern edition of *Frottole. Libro tertio* and of the other nine extant books of *frottole* published by Petrucci is in preparation by William F. Prizer for the American Institute of Musicology.

29. For further information on the *villotta*, see Fausto Torrefranca, *Il segreto del Quattrocento* (Milan, 1939). The most complete catalogue of the popular tunes used in the *villotta* is in Jeppesen, *La Frottola*, 3:13-140.

30. For further information on the performance of the *frottola*, see Prizer, "Performance Practices in the Frottola."

31. For a similar interpretation of "3" as *proportio tripla*, see Howard M. Brown, "Chansons for the Pleasure of a Florentine Patrician: Florence, Biblioteca del Conservatorio di Musica, MS Basevi 2442," *Aspects of Medieval and Renaissance Music: A Birthday Offering to Gustave Reese*, ed. by Jan LaRue (New York, 1966), p. 60.

Texts and Translations

[1.] Sonnet

Voi che ascoltate i dolorosi pianti
Del mio passato e giovenil errore,
Moveti a pietà del mio dolore
Che suspirar me fa con dolor tanti.

Et voi felici et infelici amanti,
Lassate ogni speranza hormai d'amore
Et or sola virtù drizate il core,
Lassando gli amorosi et dolci canti,

Perchè morte crudel presto ne fura
Nostra caduta et fragile speranza,
Ogni mondan piacer passa e non dura.

Virtù fa l'homo eterno per usanza
Che da po morte è chiusa in sepultura
Quella seguendo con perseveranza.

(You who hear the sorrowful tears of my former youthful errors, have pity on my sorrow that makes me sigh with such pain. And you, lovers, contented or discontented, leave now every hope of love and turn your hearts toward virtue only, leaving behind sweet love songs. For cruel death will soon be our fall and will give flight to fragile hope; every earthly delight remains not, but disappears. Virtue makes man ready for eternal life, for after death it is closed in the tomb and thus follows man even there.)

[2.] Canzone (possibly a Lauda?)

Vergine sacra, benedetta et alma,
Vergine dolce et pia,
Della terra et dil ciel primera palma,
Norma, registro et via
De la ignorata et de la mia cieca alma,
Ch'a milli errori consente;
Perdona a chi se pente
Ben ch'io sia verme, et tu del ciel regina;
Ch'a un cor contrito el ciel sempre se inclina.
Canzon, se gli è pur vero
Che'l ciel non curi l'opra, ma il core
Ancor spero pietate a tanto errore.

(Holy Virgin, blessed and pure, sweet and pious Virgin, first fruit of earth and heaven, record, standard, and guide of my blind soul that permits a thousand sins. Pardon him who repents, even though I am vermin and you, the queen of heaven; pardon him because heaven is disposed always to a contrite heart. O song, if it is true that heaven cares not for the deed, but rather for the heart, then I shall hope still for pity on my many errors.)

[3.] Madrigal

Non finsi mai d'amarte
Ma tu fingesti ben per darmi morte;
Ristora'l mio penar, ah cruda sorte,
Vinto d'ogni beltà di toi bei gesti
E da parole finte,
Gettai mio cor in foco
Non già per darti gioco;
Sperai ogn'or servir con tanta fede
Al fin del mio servir trovar mercede,
Ma tu iniqua, ingrata et impia a torto,
Ponesti a tal sorte il desir mio
Che più la morte chiedo che'l desio.

(I never merely pretended to love you, but you pretended to send me to my death. Give me respite in my pain! Ah harsh plight, I am vanquished by the very beauty of your bearing and by your false words. I threw my heart into the flames, but not to be your plaything; I hoped that such faithful service would find its reward. But you, iniquious, ungrateful, and pitiless, have unjustly placed my desire in so great a plight that I now beg more for death than for love.)

[4.] Sonnet (Petrarch)

O passi sparsi, o pensier vaghi et pronti,
O tenace memoria, o fier ardore,
O possente desir, o debil core,
O ochi mei, ochi non già, ma fonti;

O fronde, honor delle famose fronti,
O sola insegna al gemino valore;
O faticosa vita, o dolce errore,
Che me fat' ir' cercando piagge et monti;

O bel viso, ove amore insieme pose
Li sproni e'l freno, onde el mi ponge e volve
Come a lui piace, et calcitrar non vale;

O anime gentile et amorose
Se alcun ha'l mondo, et vui nude ombre et polve,
Deh, restati a veder qual è'l mio male.

(O scattered steps; O vague and ready thoughts; O constant memory; O fiery ardor; O strong desire; O weak heart; O my eyes, no longer eyes, but fountains; O fronds, honor of famous brows; O only marks of double valor; O tiresome life; O sweet error that made me search the beaches and mountains; O lovely face, where love together placed both the spurs and the reins and where I am placed and turn as he pleases and no kicking avails; O gentle, loving spirits (if such there be) and you, naked spirits, now dust, stay and see how great is my pain.)

[5.] Ballata mezzana

Piangea la donna mia
Quando da lei partia
E suspirava invece de parole.

Erave il sol presente
Et per pietà di noi, pianse egli anchora,
Et suspirando, andò verso occidente;
La piogia e'l vento alhora
Bagnomi el caldo, e spesso è il sole ardente;
Poi riasciugommi et riscaldo in poc'hora.
Ma non ha l'aqua o il vento,
El foco d'amor spento;
Nè le lachryme mie m'asciuga il sole.

(My lady cried when I left her and sighed instead of speaking. Only the sun was with us and, taking pity, it traveled westward. Then the rain and wind chilled the sun's heat, which returned and warmed me. But water and wind cannot spend love's fire nor can the sun dry my tears.)

[6.] Ballata mezzana (Petrarch)

Perchè quel che mi trasse ad amar prima
Altrui colpa mi toglia,
Del mio fermo voler già non mi svoglia.

Tra le chiume de l'or nascose il laccio
Al qual mi strinse amore;
E da begli occhi mosse in freddo g*h*iaccio
Che mi passò nel core
Con la virtù d'un subito splendore,
Che d'ogn'altra sua voglia,
Sol rimembrando, ancor l'anima spoglia.

(Even though that which first drew me to love is taken from me, yet my steadfast desire shall not take me away. Among the golden tresses hides the trap with which love ensnares me, and from those lovely eyes the cold ice entered my heart with the force of a sudden splendor that removed any other wish. Only remembering plunders again my heart.)

[7.] Villotta

Dillà da l'acqua sta la mia amorosa
E mai vederla posso una sol fiata,
Per una mala vecchia disdegnosa,
Che la tien sempre in camera serata.
O rancagnata, O vechia mata,
Siagurata, soza et sporcha,
Viso d'orcha, *rabbiosa,*
Tu tien sconta la mia 'morosa.
S'tu vorà, s'tu non vorà,
L'haverò, la m'haverà.

Se vederla potessi una sol volta,
Mai l'aspettar non me rincresceria;
Ma questa mala vecchia me l'ha tolta
Che più non vedi la speranza mia.
O che pazzia, de'sta Badia
Vecchia ria, bronza coperta,
Ben deserta, storna et stolta,
Ch'ella m'alde et non me scolta.
S'tu vorà. . . .

Oimè, che alcun non ho che me conforta
Poichè 'sta vechia più da me, lontana
Quella che, nel suo petto, mio cor porta:
Splendente più che in ciel stella Diana.
O vecchia insana, ria, vilana,
Ruffiana, storta e sbiga,
Vecchia striga, fusti morta,
Denti longhi e bocha storta.
S'tu vorà. . . .

(There across the water is my beloved, and I can see her not even once because an envious, scornful old woman keeps her in a locked room. O flat-faced, mad, wicked, foul, dirty, rabid ogress; you keep my beloved hidden away. If you want or if you don't, I'll have her and she'll have me.

If I were able to see her even once, I shouldn't mind waiting for her. But this damned old woman has torn her from me so that I can no longer see her, my hope. O how foolish is this village. Old tyrant, sanctimonious hypocrite, deserted by all; twisted fool, for she listens and doesn't hear me. If you want or if you don't, I'll have her and she'll have me.

Alas, I have no one to comfort me because this old woman takes away from me her who carries my heart in her breast. She is more splendid than the star Diana in the heavens. O old moron, tyrant, villain, ruffian, twisted and crooked old witch, I wish you were dead; long of tooth with twisted mouth. If you want or if you don't, I'll have her and she'll have me.)

[8.] Madrigal (Petrarch)

Non al suo amante più Diana piacque,
Quando per tal ventura tutta ignuda
La vide in mezzo delle gelide acque;

Che a me la pastorella alpestra e cruda
Posta a bagnar un legiadretto velo,
Che a l'aura il vago et biondo capel chiuda;

Tal che mi fece hor quando egli arde il cielo,
Tutto tremmar d'un amoroso gielo.

(No more did Diana please her lover when, by fortune, he saw her nude in the midst of the icy waters, than was I pleased by the wild shepherdess there to bathe the light veil that covers the lovely blond hair in the gentle breeze. So much did it please me that now, while the heavens burn, I shiver in an amorous chill.)

[9.] Strambotto (Serafino dall'Aquila)

Del mio sì grande et del tuo amor sì poco,
Non ha difetto amor ma tua natura.

Ch'io veggio frutti in un medesmo loco,
L'un dolce e l'altro mai non si matura;
Veggio la cera e'l fango ad un sol foco,
L'una se liquefà, l'altro se indura:
Così cocendo noi d'un foco amore,
Tu te indurasti, a me anci se sfece il core.

(For my great love and for yours so slight, not love itself but your nature is to blame. I see fruits from the same tree, the one sweet and the other that never matures. I see wax and clay on the same fire: the one melts and the other hardens. Thus are we cooking on a fire of love: you become hard, and my heart melts.)

[10.] Barzelletta

Poichè in van mia mente sogna
E i passi ho sparsi al vento,
Da qui innanti più contento,
Canterò senza vergogna:

"Vegnando da Bologna,
La scarpa mi fa male;
Tandarondarindunda."

Non sia alcun che in donna speri
De trovar pietà giamai
Che fallaci illor pensieri
Sempre so perchè provai.
Hor che amor me'l fai
Canterò senza vergogna:

"Vegnando da Bologna. . . ."

(Since my mind dreams in vain and allows my steps to wander where they may, henceforth shall I sing without care: "Coming from Bologna, my shoes hurt my feet, Tandarondarindunda." No one should hope that a woman will have pity on him, as such a thought is always false; this I know because I have tried. Since love treats me thus, I shall sing without care: "Coming from Bologna, my shoes hurt my feet. Tandarondarindunda.")

[11.] Villotta

Un cavalier de Spagna
Cavalca per la via,
Da piè de la montagna,
Cantando per amor d'una fantina:

"Voltate in qua, do bella donzellina,
Voltate un poco a me, per cortesia,
Dolce speranza mia,
Che moro per tuo amor;
Bella fantina, i't'ho donato el cor."

Apresso una fontana
Vide sentar la bella
Soletta in terra piana,
Con una ghirlanda di fresca herbecina.

"Voltate in qua, do bella donzellina,
Voltate un poco a me, lucente stella,
Deh, non m'esser ribella:
Che moro per tuo amor.
Bella fantina, i't'ho donato el cor."

(A cavalier of Spain rode on his way. Coming from the foot of the mountains, he sang for the love of a maid: "Turn to me, O lovely damsel, kindly turn to me for a while. My sweet hope, I die for your love; lovely maid, I have given you my heart." Near a fountain, he saw the lovely girl sitting alone in the meadow, wearing a garland of fresh grasses. "Turn to me, O lovely damsel, turn to me for a while, my shining star. O don't resist me, for I die for your love; lovely maid, I have given you my heart.")

[12] Canzone (Petrarch)

Amor, se voi ch'io torni al giogo antico,
Come par che tu mostri, un altra prova
Maravigliosa et nova,
Per domarme convienti vincer pria.
Il mio amato thesoro in terra trova,
Che m'è nascosto, ond'io son si mendico
E'l cor saggio e pudico
Ove sole albergar la vita mia:
E s'egli è ver che tua potenza sia

Nel ciel sì grande come si ragiona,
Et nel abisso, perchè qui fra noi
Quel che tu vali e poi
Credo che'l senta ogni gentil persona,
Ritogli a morte quel ch'ella n'ha tolto,
Et ripon le tue insigne nel bel volto.

(Love, if you wish me to return to your yoke, then I must have of you one other proof, miraculous and extraordinary, before I return to you, conquered. Lift my dear loved one from the earth that now hides her from me; I am made a beggar for want of that wise, chaste heart where my life once lived. And if it is true, as they say, that your power is as great in heaven as in the depths of hell (for here on earth every noble person knows your power), then take back from death her whom he has taken and replace your sign on her lovely face.)

[13.] Canzone (Petrarch)

Se 'l pensier che mi strugge
Com'è pungente e saldo
Così vestisse d'un color conforme,
Forse tal m'arde e fugge,
Ch'havria parte del caldo,
Et desteriase amor là dove hor dorme;
Men solitarie l'orme
Foran de' miei piè lassi
Per campagnie e per colli
Men gli occhi ad ogn'hor molli;
Ardendo lei che come un ghiaccio stassi
E non lassa in me dramma
Che non sia foco e fiamma.

(If the strong, painful thought that consumes me were to be dressed in a suitable garb, she who inflames me and flees would then partake of this loving ardor and awaken love where now it sleeps. Less solitary then would be my steps through countryside and hills and less often would these eyes weep, burning for her who is like unmoving ice and yet leaves of me not the smallest part that is not fire and flame.)

[14.] Villotta

Le son tre fantinelle,
Tutte tre da maridare;
Tandan dan dan daritondella,
Tan daridundella.
Le son tre fantinelle,
Tutte tre da maridare.

Ch'andavan a lo giardino,
A lo giardino per amor;
Tandan dan dan daritondella,
Tan daridundella.
Le son. . . .

Et per coglier le rose,
Le rose con li fiori;
Tandan dan dan daritondella,
Tan daridundella.
Le son. . . .

Per far un capelleto
Al suo caro fin amor;
Tandan dan dan daritondella,
Tan daridundella.
Le son. . . .

E da portar le feste,
E le feste principale;
Tandan dan dan daritondella,
Tan daridundella.
Le son. . . .

Et per quella di Pasqua
E quella di Nattale;
Tandan dan dan daritondella,
Tan daridundella.
Le son. . . .

E quella di San Zuane
Che vien da mezza istade;
Tandan dan dan daritondella,
Tan daridundella.
Le son. . . .

(There were three pretty maids to be married. Tandan dan dan daritondella, tan daridundella. There were three pretty maids to be married.

Who went into the garden for love. Tandan dan dan daritondella, tan daridundella. There were three pretty maids to be married.

And to pick the roses and the other flowers. Tandan dan dan daritondella, tan daridundella. There were three pretty maids to be married.

To make a garland for their love. Tandan dan dan daritondella, tan daridundella. There were three pretty maids to be married.

And to wear at the feasts, the important feasts. Tandan dan dan daritondella, tan daridundella. There were three pretty maids to be married.

And for the feast of Easter and for the feast of Christmas. Tandan dan dan daritondella, tan daridundella. There were three pretty maids to be married.

And for the feast of St. John, that comes in the middle of summer. Tandan dan dan daritondella, tan daridundella. There were three pretty maids to be married.)

[15.] Villotta

Vrai dieu d'amor qui me conforterà
Che'l mio amor si m'à lassa;
Farira fararirum.
Ch'io sum fora di presum;
O faralilalum,
Ch'io sum fora di presum
Et vo cantando ogni hora:

"O tient alora,
A l'umbre d'un bel *pino.*
Ucelino, bel ucelino,
Come sa tu ben cantar?"
Farililum farirerum.

(True god of love, who will comfort me, now that my love is gone? Farira fararirum. For I am out of jail. O faralilalum, for I am out of jail and want to sing at every moment, "O rest in the shadow of a pretty pine. Little bird, pretty little bird, however do you sing so well?" Farililum farirerum.)

[16.] Canzone (Petrarch)

Ben mi credea passar mio tempo homai
Come passato havea questi anni a dietro,
Senza altro studio e senza novi ingegni:
Hor poichè da madonna io non impetro
L'usata aita, a che condutto m'hai.
Tu'l vedi, amor, che tal arte m'insegni.
Non so s'i' me ne sdegni;
Che in questa età mi fai divenir ladro
Del bel lume leggiadro,
Senza qual non vivrei in tanti affanni.
Così havessi i primi anni
Preso lo stil ch'or prender mi bisogna;
Che'n giovenil fallire è men vergognia.

(I believed that I could spend my life henceforth as I have spent past years, without new studies or insights. Since now I fail to find from my lady the accustomed aid, you see, love, where you have led me with your teaching. I know not if I should feel shame, that, at my age, you make me into a thief of that playful light without which I could not bear my great woe. Thus might I better have played the part in youth I must now play, for in youthful errors is there less shame.)

[17.] Canzone (Luca Valenziano Dertonese)

Come senza costei
Viver potrò, che questa chiara luce
È pur quella che in me vita produce?
Vorei anzi'l partir fusse'l mio fine;
Ma come morir posso
Dinanzi agli occhi soi che son mia vita?
Haimè il sguardo gentil che m'ha percosso,
Haimè quel aureo crine,
Haimè ch'io lascio la beltà infinita,
Ahi dura dipartita!
Qual cieco me n'andrò dove non luce;
Madonna el mio martir miser adduce.

(How shall I live without her who is my light and she who gives me life? I should wish to die before my appointed time, yet how can I die before those eyes that are my life? Alas, I must leave this infinite beauty! Alas, how painful is the parting! Like a blind man I shall wander where light enters not; my lady, my martyrdom makes me wretched.)

[18.] Villotta

E discalza e discalzetta
D'amor, in camisola,
Ch'andavolo recercando,
El suo caro bel fin amore.

(Because of love, she went, without stockings and clad only in a bodice, in search of her own true love.)

[19.] Ballata mezzana

Alma gentil, che di tua vaga spoglia,
E di toi bei costumi il mondo ornasti,
E al tuo partir in pianto mi lasciasti.

Solea con la beltà starsi honestate
Alla dolce ombra di toi chiari sguardi,
E dentro al divin volto
Che'l ciel diede et hor per se l'ha tolto,
E ciascun parea dir la tua beltade,
Minor vedrai si poi d'amor non ardi,
Ma pur la castitade
Agli honesti pensier sol dava loco,
Onde aspetti aguagliando il g*h*iaccio al foco.
Tanti cuor fatti innamorati et casti,
Quante volte ad altrui tu te mostrasti.

(Gentle spirit, who, with your lovely bearing and with your graceful custom, adorned the earth and left me in tears at your parting, once beauty and honesty were united in the sweet shadow of your transparent glance. And within your divine visage that heaven had given you and now takes away, your beauty spoke to all who saw you. Yet, without love, your beauty seems less. Only chastity was in your thoughts, thus making the ice of chastity and the fire of love equal. You have rendered enamoured yet chaste the hearts of all who have seen you.)

[20.] Ballata-madrigal

Amor, che me tormenti
Et me apresenti il bel sguardo suave
Di quella che di me pietà non have

Perchè non mostri a lei sì spesso il foco
Che me consuma el core,
Come a me mostri sua beltà infinita?
Forsi che saperia che cosa è amore
E come se sostrage a poco a poco
Un che lontan de la speranza sia,
Ahi dura sorte mia.
Madonna, me non cura e certo vede
Che altro non regna in me, che amor e fede.

(Love, who tortures me and makes me know the sweet, soft glance of her who has no pity for me, why do you not show her the fire that consumes my heart, just as you show me her infinite beauty? Perhaps then she might learn what love is and how one can languish slowly, left without hope. Alas, my harsh plight! My lady cares not for me and yet she surely sees that only love and faith reign within me.)

[21.] Villotta

L'ultimo dì de maggio,
Un bel matino per la fresca rosata,
Se n'andava la bella allo giardino,
Da vinti damigelle accompagnata;
Ogni una innamorata,
Gentil, accorta e bella.
Tandaridondella.
Oimè, che l'è pur quella
Che m'ha ligato il cor, che me l'ha tolto
Con la beltà del suo splendente volto.

C'una ghirlanda di bel gelsomino,
Sopra la treccia ornata,
Lieta lei se n'andava al suo camino,
Il primo giorno de Pasqua rosata.
O felice giornata,
Joconda, allegra, et bella.
Tandaridondella. . . .

(The last day of May, at cool dawn of a beautiful day, the lovely girl went into the garden, accompanied by twenty pretty young maids—each one in love, gentle, demure, and lovely. Tandaridondella. Alas, it is she who has chained my heart, who has captured me with the beauty of her bright visage.

With a garland of sweet gelsomine that crowns her braids, she gracefully went her way on the first day of rosy Easter. O happy day, merry, gay, and lovely. Tandaridondella. Alas, it is she who has chained my heart, who has captured me with the beauty of her bright visage.)

[22.] Villotta

E dapoi che 'l sol dal monte
Se levava, me n'andava
Dove spesso passegiava,
La mia nympha, a pe' d'un fonte.

(After the sun rose from behind the mountains, I went where oft my nymph passed at the base of a fountain.)

Canzoni · Frottole · & Capitoli · Da Diversi
Excellentissimi Musici Composti ·
Nouamente Stampati
& Correcti ·

Libro Primo · De La Croce ·

Plate I. *Libro primo de la croce,* title page.
(Courtesy, Österreichische Nationalbibliothek, Vienna.)

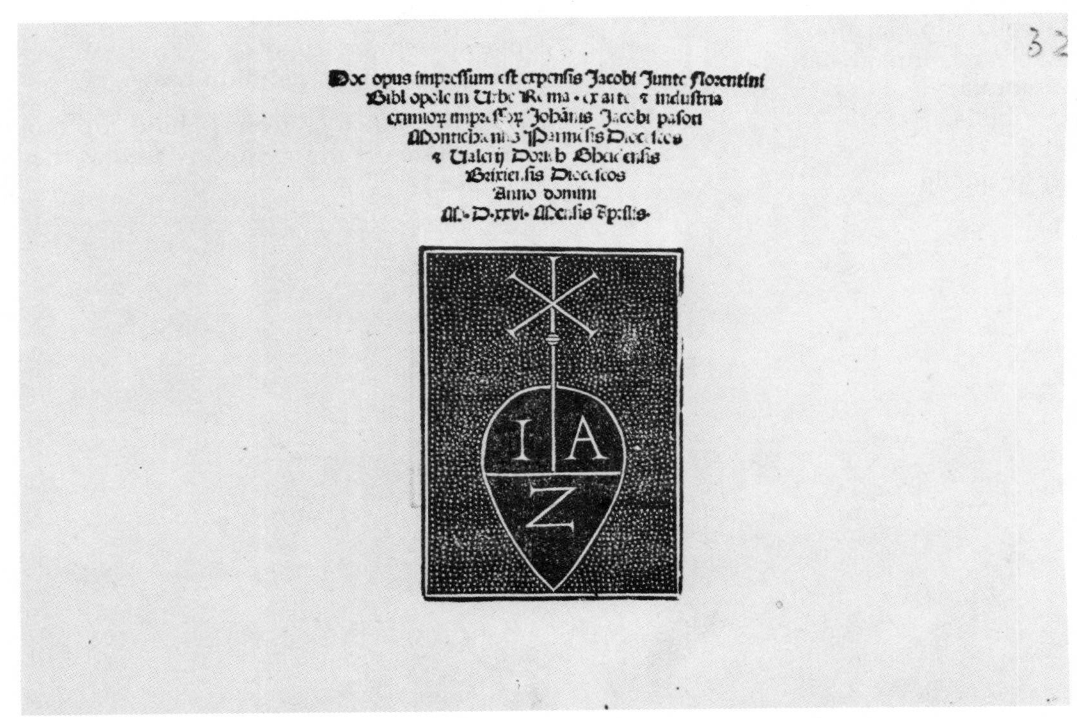

Hoc opus impressum est expensis Jacobi Junte Florentini
Bibliopole in Urbe Roma · ex arte & industria
eximiorum impressorum Johannis Jacobi pasoti
Montichiarensis Parmensis Diocesos
& Valerij Dorich Ghedensis
Brixiensis Diocesos
Anno domini
M · D · xxvi · Mensis Aprilis ·

Plate II. *Libro primo de la croce,* colophon.
(Courtesy, Österreichische Nationalbibliothek, Vienna.)

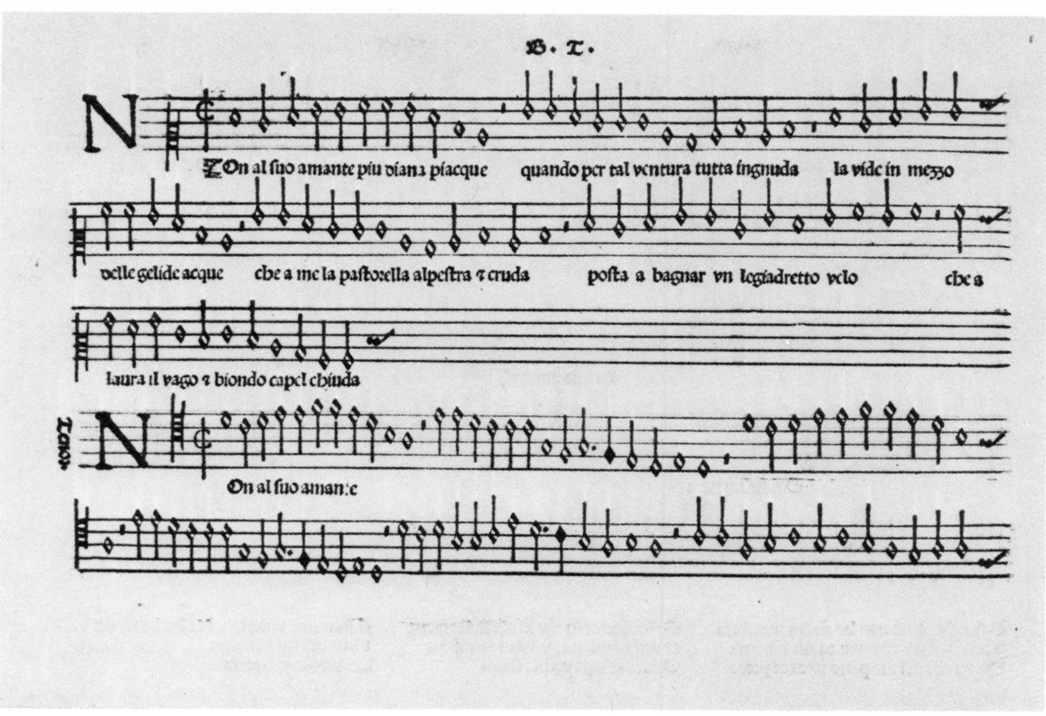

Plate III. *Libro primo de la croce,* f. 12v. Beginning of Cantus and Tenor of *Non al suo amante* (No. [8]), showing the ascription to B[artolomeo] T[romboncino]. (Courtesy, Österreichische Nationalbibliothek, Vienna.)

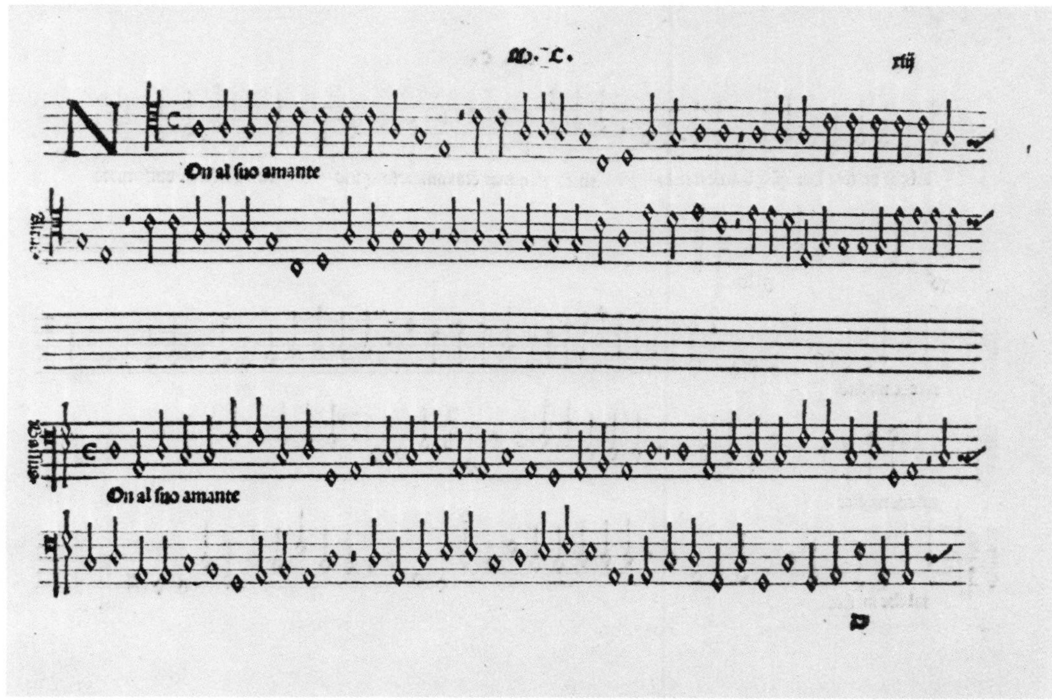

Plate IV. *Libro primo de la croce,* f. 13r. Beginning of Altus and Bassus of *Non al suo amante* (No. [8]), showing the ascription to M[archetto] C[ara]. (Courtesy, Österreichische Nationalbibliothek, Vienna.)

LIBRO PRIMO DE LA CROCE

[1.] Voi che ascoltate

[2.] Vergine sacra

15
pri– me– – ra pal– ma, Nor– ma, re– gis– tro et
– ra pal– ma, Nor– ma, re– gis– tro et
–me– – ra pal– ma, Nor– ma, re– gis– tro et
pri– me– ra pal– ma, Nor– ma, re– gis– tro et

20
vi– a De la i–gno–ra– ta et de la mia cie–ca al– ma,
vi– a De la i–gno–
vi– a De la i–gno–ra– ta et de la mia cie–ca al– ma, De la i–gno–
vi– a De la i–gno–

25
Ch'a mil– li er– ro– ri con–
–ra– ta et de la mia cie– ca al– ma, Ch'a mil– li er– ro– ri con–
–ra– ta et de la mia cie– ca al– ma, Ch'a mil– li er– ro– ri con–
–ra– ta et de la mia cie– ca al– ma, Ch'a mil– li er– ro– ri con–

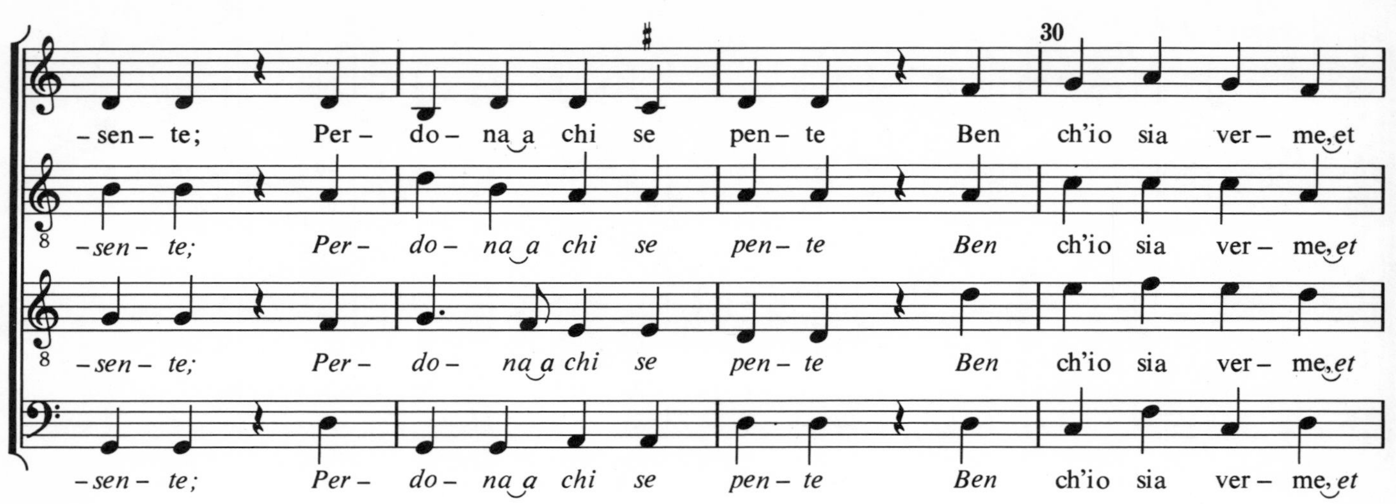
30
–sen – te; Per – do – na a chi se pen – te Ben ch'io sia ver – me, et
–sen – te; Per – do – na a chi se pen – te Ben ch'io sia ver – me, et
–sen – te; Per – do – na a chi se pen – te Ben ch'io sia ver – me, et
–sen – te; Per – do – na a chi se pen – te Ben ch'io sia ver – me, et

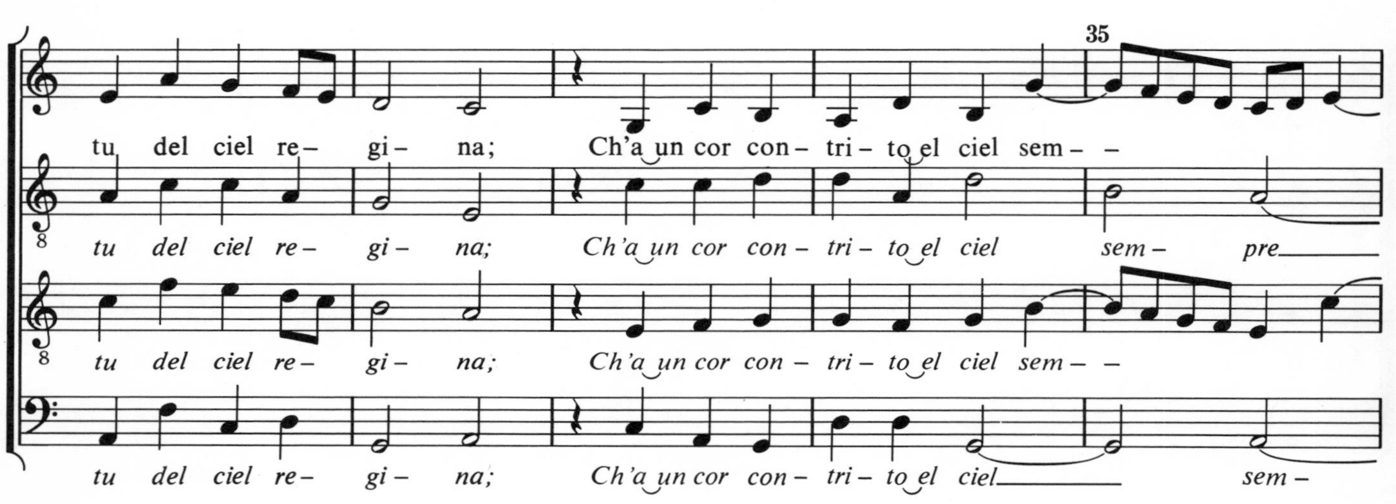
35
tu del ciel re – gi – na; Ch'a un cor con – tri – to el ciel sem – –
tu del ciel re – gi – na; Ch'a un cor con – tri – to el ciel sem – pre
tu del ciel re – gi – na; Ch'a un cor con – tri – to el ciel sem – –
tu del ciel re – gi – na; Ch'a un cor con – tri – to el ciel sem –

– pre se in – cli – na.
se in – cli – na.
– pre se in – – cli – na.
– pre se in – – cli – na.

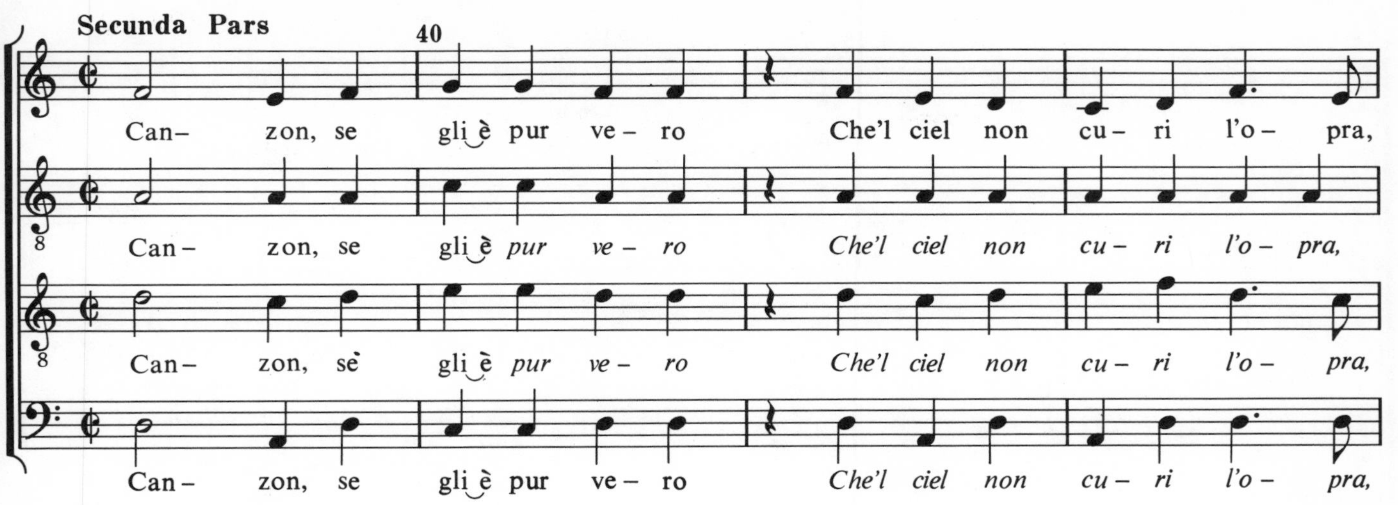
Secunda Pars
40
Can– zon, se gli è pur ve – ro Che'l ciel non cu – ri l'o – pra,
Can – zon, se gli è pur ve – ro Che'l ciel non cu – ri l'o – pra,
Can – zon, se gli è pur ve – ro Che'l ciel non cu – ri l'o – pra,
Can – zon, se gli è pur ve – ro Che'l ciel non cu – ri l'o – pra,

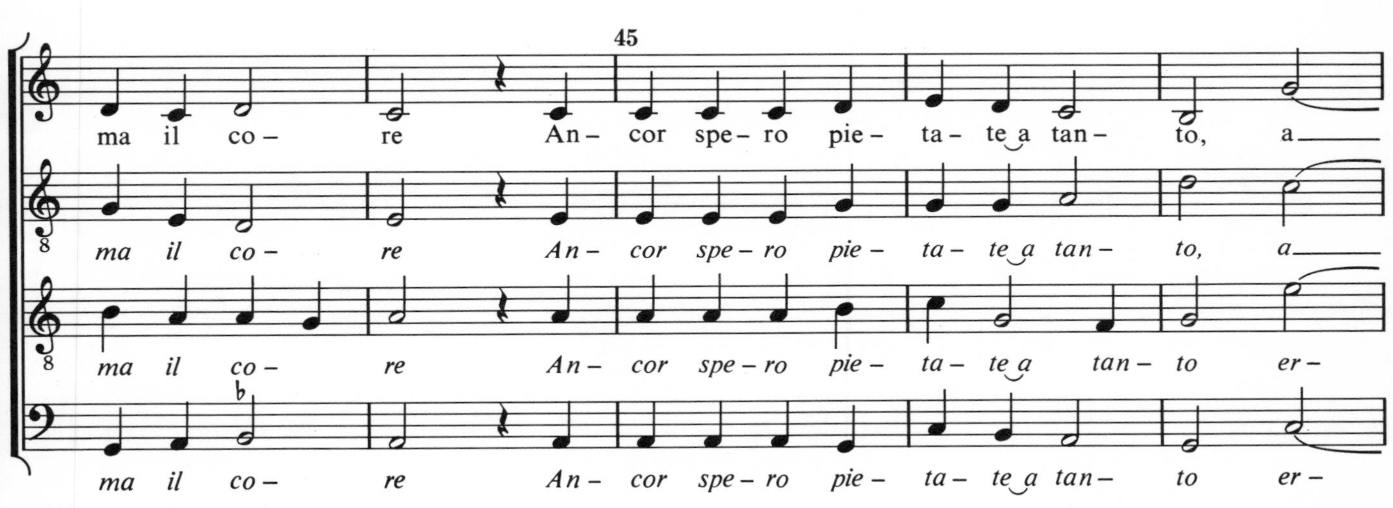
45
ma il co – re An – cor spe – ro pie – ta – te a tan – to, a
ma il co – re An – cor spe – ro pie – ta – te a tan – to, a
ma il co – re An – cor spe – ro pie – ta – te a tan – to er –
ma il co – re An – cor spe – ro pie – ta – te a tan – to er –

50
tan – – – to er – ro – re, a
tan – to er – ro – – re, a
– – ro – – re, er – ro – re, a
– ro – re, er – ro – re, a

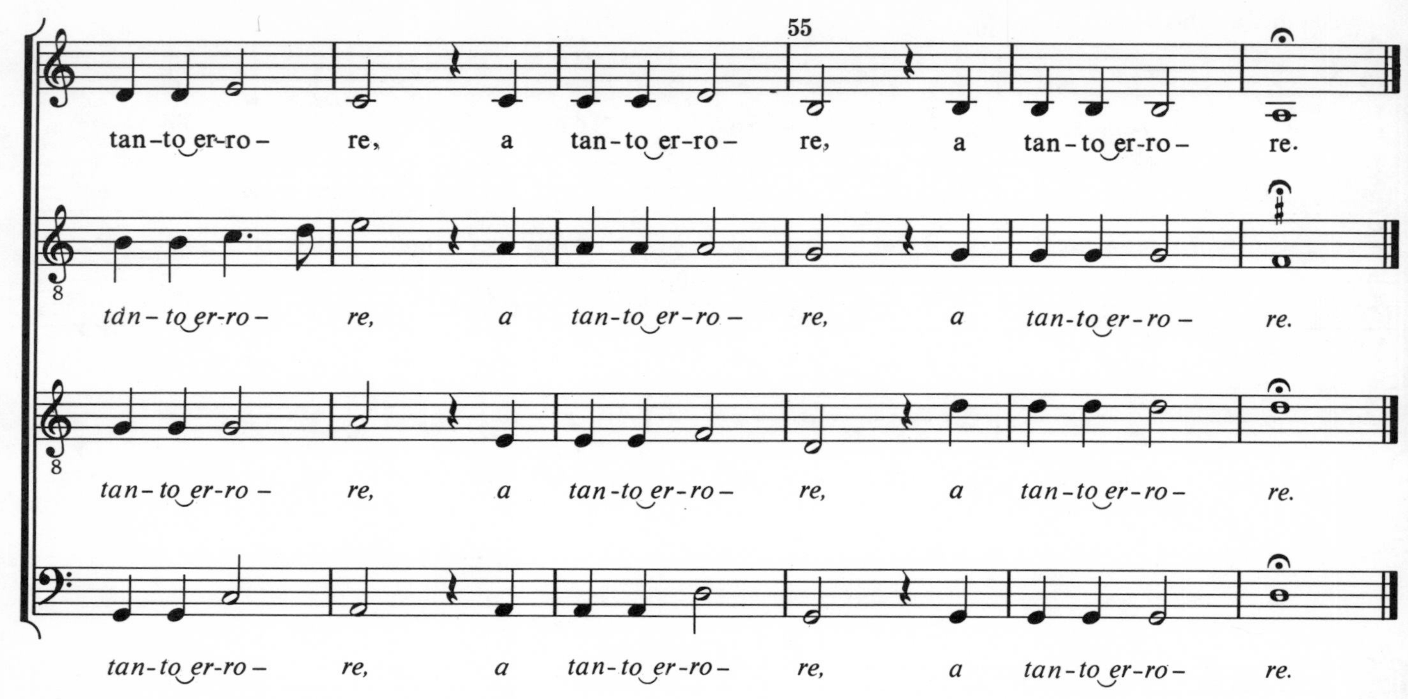

[3.] Non finsi mai d'amarte

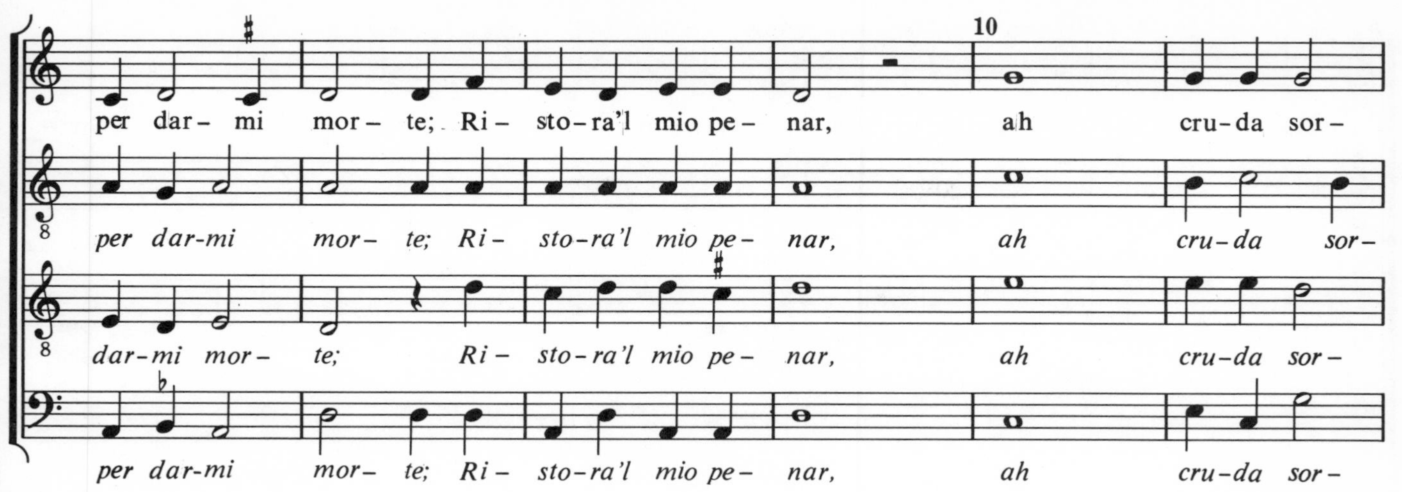
10
per dar- mi mor- te; Ri- sto- ra'l mio pe- nar, ah cru- da sor-
per dar-mi mor- te; Ri- sto-ra'l mio pe- nar, ah cru-da sor-
dar-mi mor- te; Ri- sto-ra'l mio pe- nar, ah cru-da sor-
per dar-mi mor- te; Ri- sto-ra'l mio pe- nar, ah cru-da sor-

15
-te, ah cru-da sor- te, Vin- to d'o-gni bel- tà di
-te, ah cru-da sor- te, Vin- to d'o-gni bel- tà di
-te, ah cru-da sor- te, Vin- to d'o-gni bel- tà di
-te, ah cru-da sor- te, Vin- to d'o-gni bel- tà di

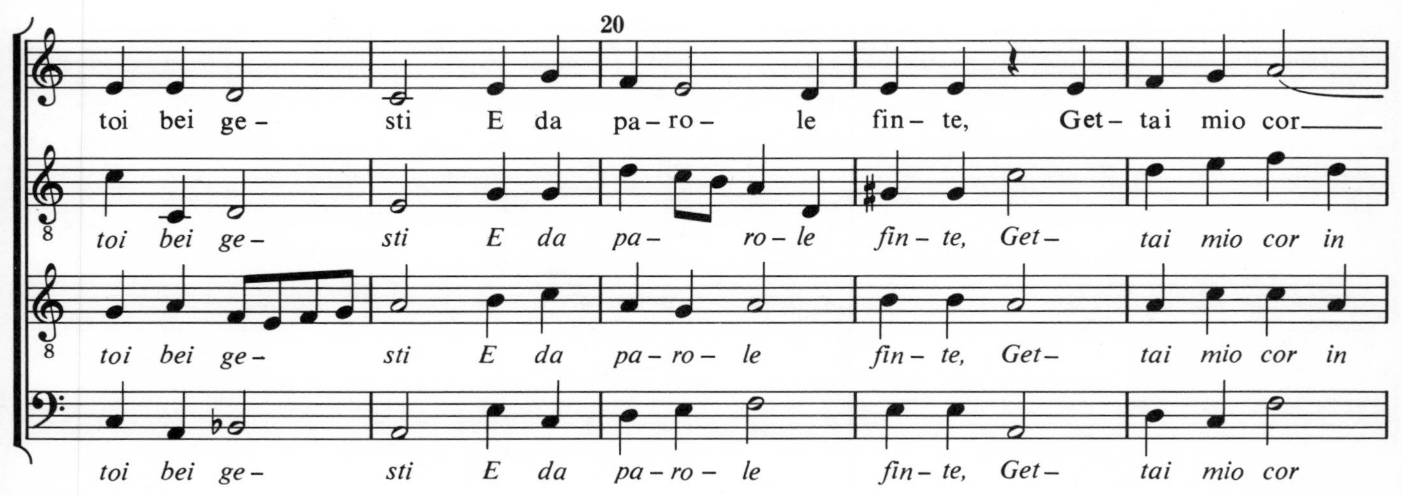
20
toi bei ge- sti E da pa- ro- le fin- te, Get- tai mio cor
toi bei ge- sti E da pa- ro- le fin- te, Get- tai mio cor in
toi bei ge- sti E da pa- ro- le fin- te, Get- tai mio cor in
toi bei ge- sti E da pa- ro- le fin- te, Get- tai mio cor

25
in fo– co Non già per dar– – ti gio– co; Spe–
fo– co Non già per dar– ti– gio– co; Spe–rai
fo– co Non già per dar– ti– gio– co; Spe–rai o–
in fo– co Non già per dar– ti– gio– co; Spe–

30
–rai o– gn'or ser– vir con tan– – ta fe– de Al
o– gn'or ser– vir con tan– ta fe– de Al fin
– gn'or ser– vir con tan– – ta fe– de Al fin del
–rai o– gn'or ser– vir con tan– – ta fe– de Al

35
fin del mio ser– vir tro– var mer– ce– de, Ma
del mio ser– vir tro– var mer– ce– de, Ma tu i–
mio ser– vir tro– var mer– ce– de, Ma
fin del mio ser– vir tro– var, mer– ce– de, Ma

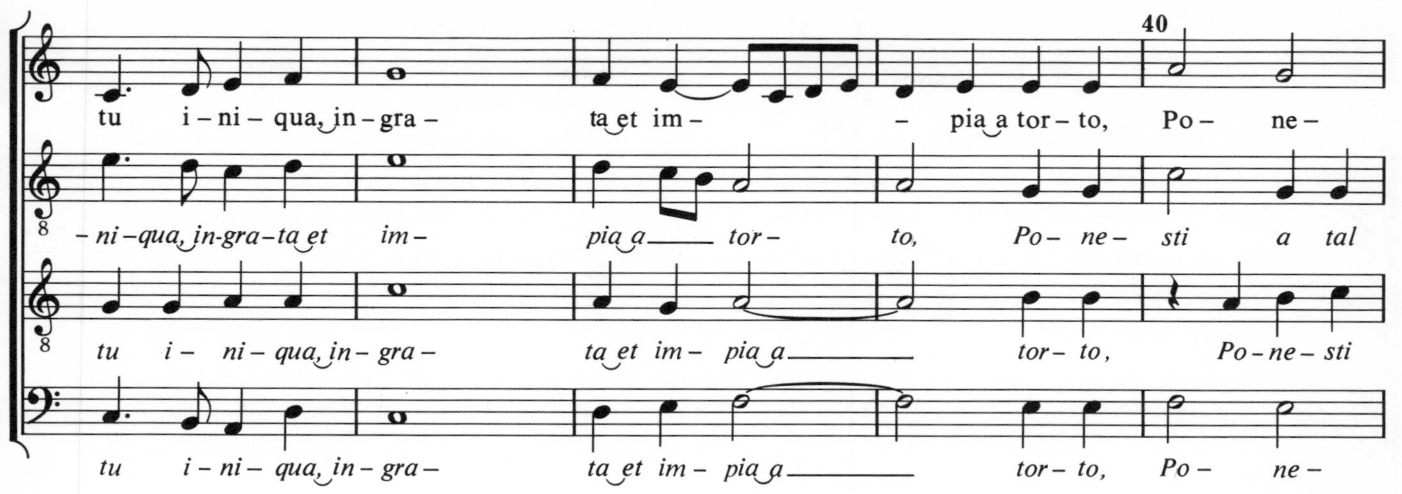
40
tu i – ni – qua, in – gra – ta et im – – pia a tor – to, Po – ne –
– ni – qua, in-gra – ta et im – pia a tor – to, Po – ne – sti a tal
tu i – ni – qua, in – gra – ta et im – pia a tor – to, Po – ne – sti
tu i – ni – qua, in – gra – ta et im – pia a tor – to, Po – ne –

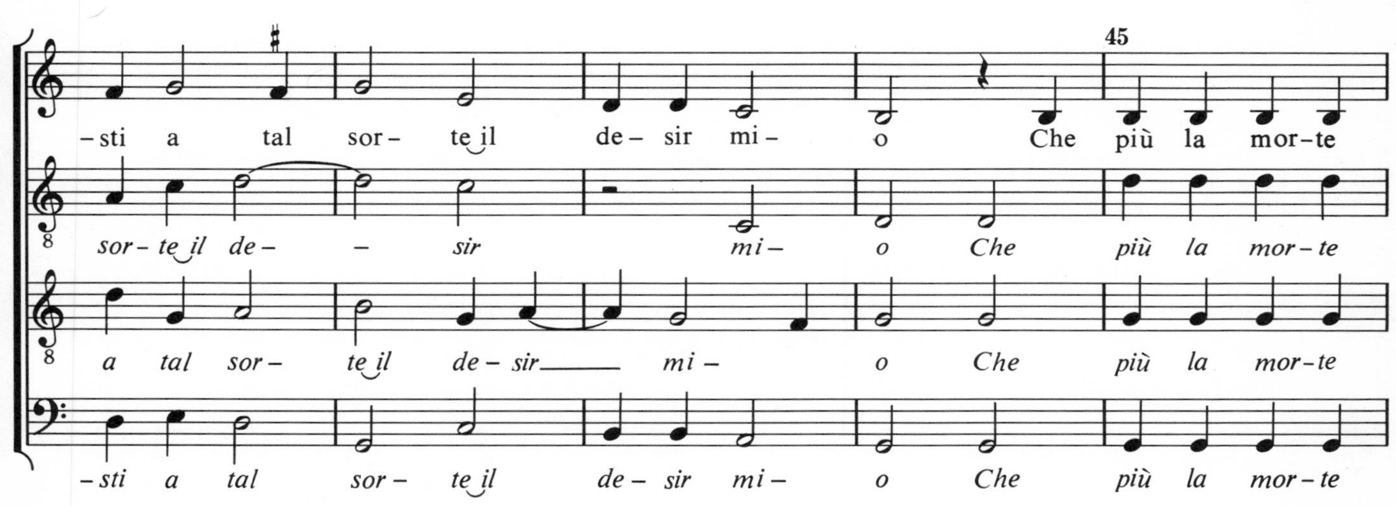
45
– sti a tal sor – te il de – sir mi – o Che più la mor-te
sor – te il de – – sir mi – o Che più la mor – te
a tal sor – te il de – sir mi – o Che più la mor-te
– sti a tal sor – te il de – sir mi – o Che più la mor – te

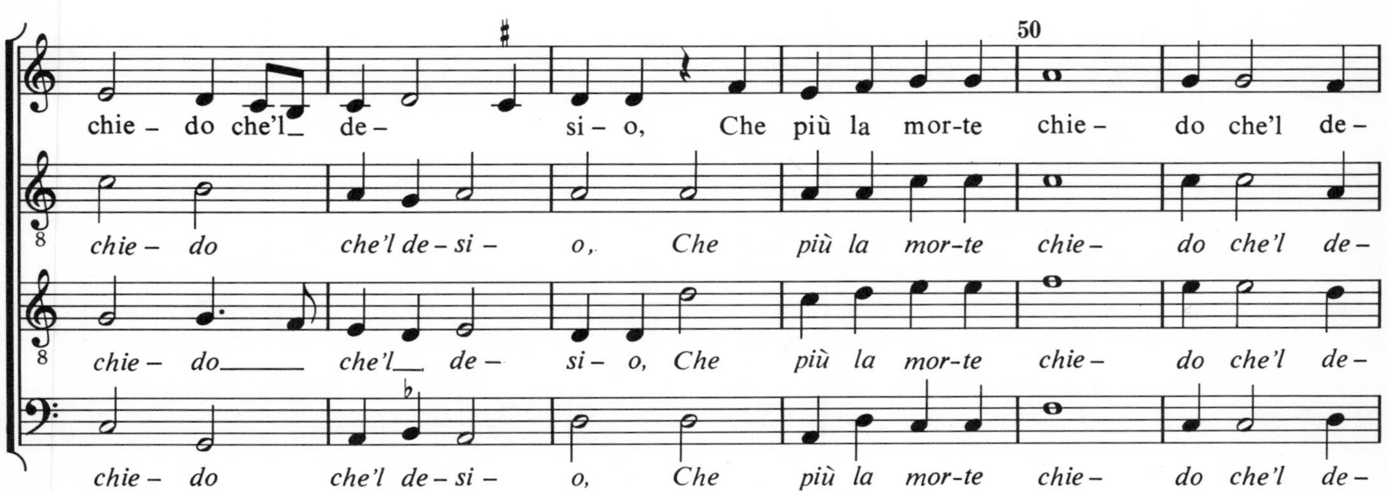
50
chie – do che'l de – si – o, Che più la mor-te chie – do che'l de –
chie – do che'l de – si – o, Che più la mor-te chie – do che'l de –
chie – do che'l de – si – o, Che più la mor-te chie – do che'l de –
chie – do che'l de – si – o, Che più la mor-te chie – do che'l de –

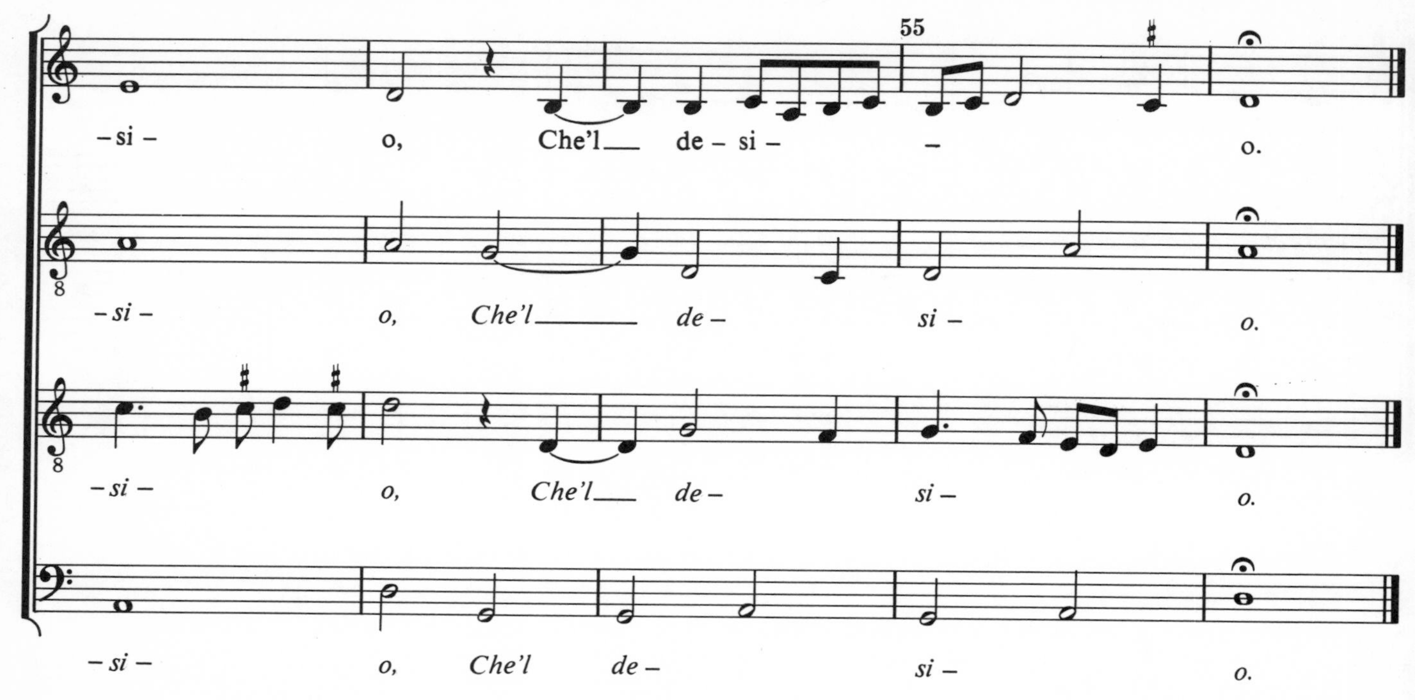

[4.] O passi sparsi

Petrarch

Sebastian Festa

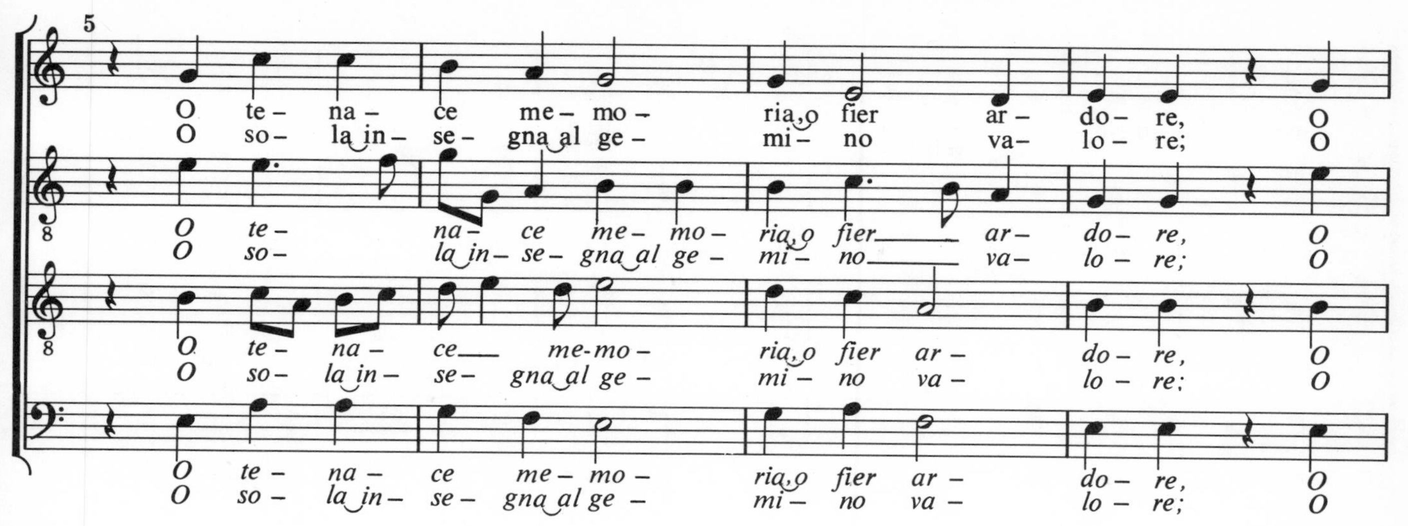
5
O te– na– ce me– mo– ria, o fier ar– do– re, O
O so– la in– se– gna al ge– mi– no va– lo– re; O
O te– na– ce me– mo– ria, o fier ar– do– re, O
O so– la in– se– gna al ge– mi– no va– lo– re; O
O te– na– ce me-mo– ria, o fier ar– do– re, O
O so– la in– se– gna al ge– mi– no va– lo– re; O
O te– na– ce me– mo– ria, o fier ar– do– re, O
O so– la in– se– gna al ge– mi– no va– lo– re; O

10
pos– sen– te de– sir, o de– bil co– re, O o– chi
fa– ti – co– sa vi– ta, o dol– ce er–ro– re, Che me fat'
pos– sen-te de– sir, o de– bil co– re, O o– chi
fa– ti–co– sa vi– ta, o dol– ce er–ro– re, Che me fat'
pos– sen– te de– sir, o de– bil co– re, O o– chi
fa– ti – co– sa vi– ta, o dol– ce er– ro– re, Che me fat'
pos– sen– te de– sir, o de– bil co– re, O o– chi
fa– ti – co– sa vi– ta, o dol– ce er– ro– re, Che me fat'

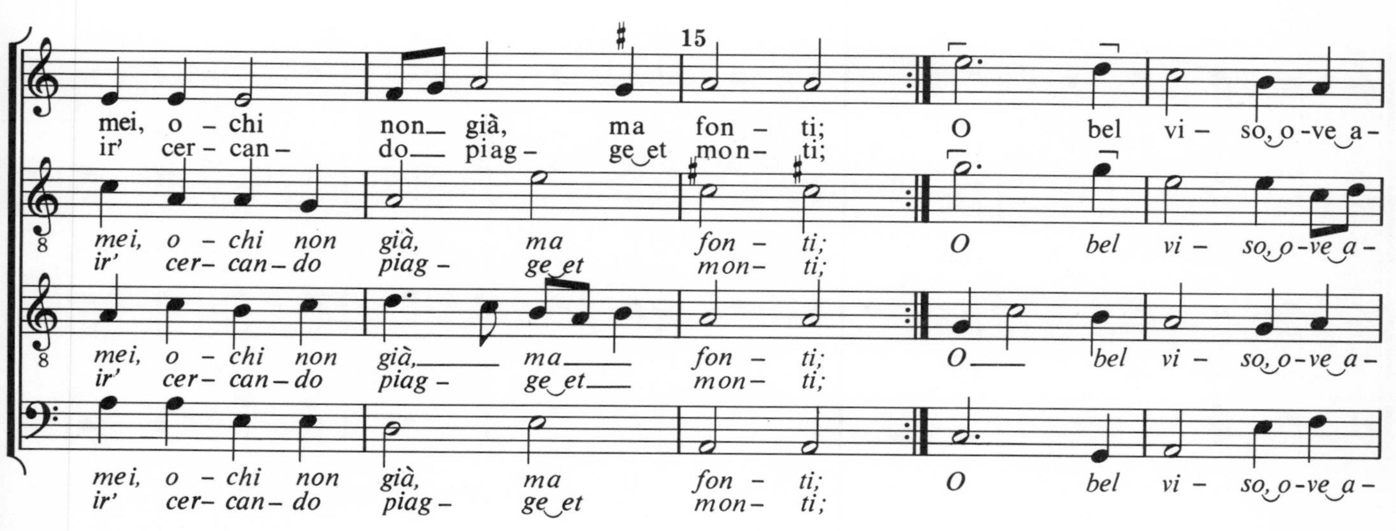
15
mei, o – chi non già, ma fon– ti; O bel vi – so, o-ve a–
ir' cer – can– do piag– ge et mon– ti;
mei, o– chi non già, ma fon – ti; O bel vi – so, o-ve a–
ir' cer– can– do piag– ge et mon– ti;
mei, o – chi non già, ma fon – ti; O bel vi – so, o-ve a–
ir' cer– can– do piag – ge et mon– ti;
mei, o – chi non già, ma fon – ti; O bel vi – so, o-ve a–
ir' cer– can– do piag – ge et mon– ti;

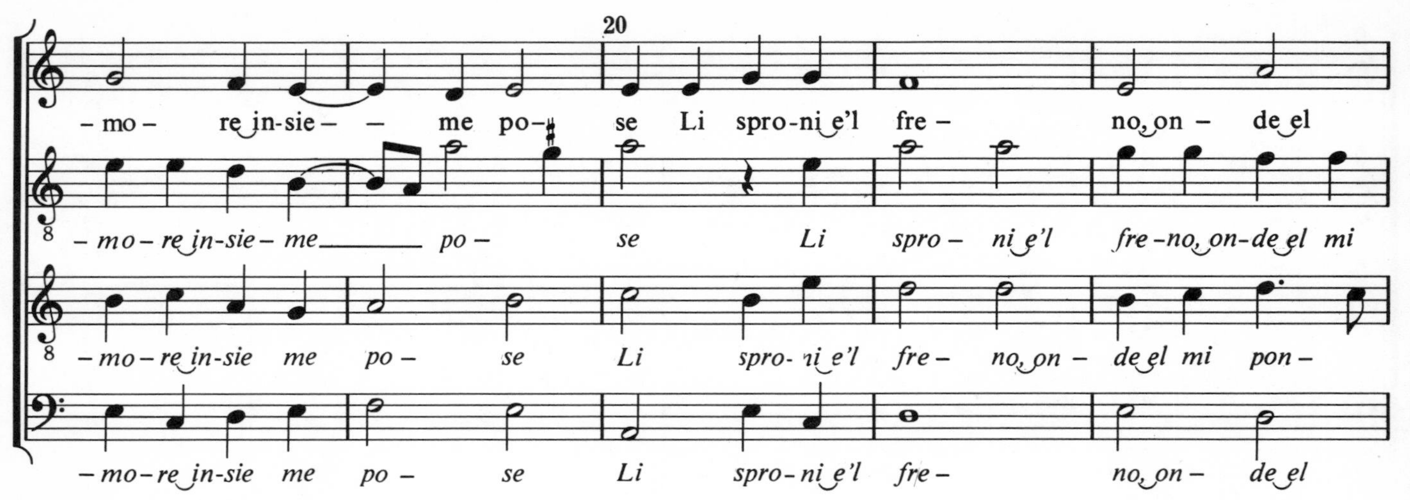
20
– mo – re in-sie – – me po- se Li spro-ni e'l fre – no, on – de el
– mo – re in-sie – me po – se Li spro – ni e'l fre – no, on-de el mi
– mo – re in-sie me po – se Li spro- ni e'l fre – no, on – de el mi pon –
– mo – re in-sie me po – se Li spro – ni e'l fre – no, on – de el

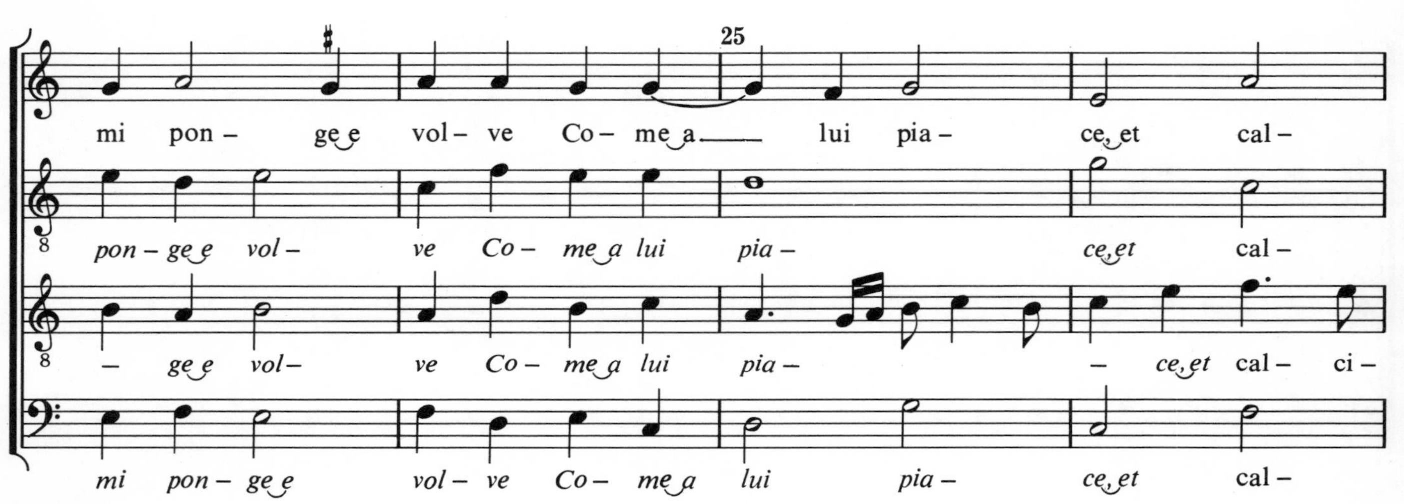
25
mi pon – ge e vol – ve Co – me a lui pia – ce, et cal –
pon – ge e vol – ve Co – me a lui pia – ce, et cal –
– ge e vol – ve Co – me a lui pia – – ce, et cal – ci –
mi pon – ge e vol – ve Co – me a lui pia – ce, et cal –

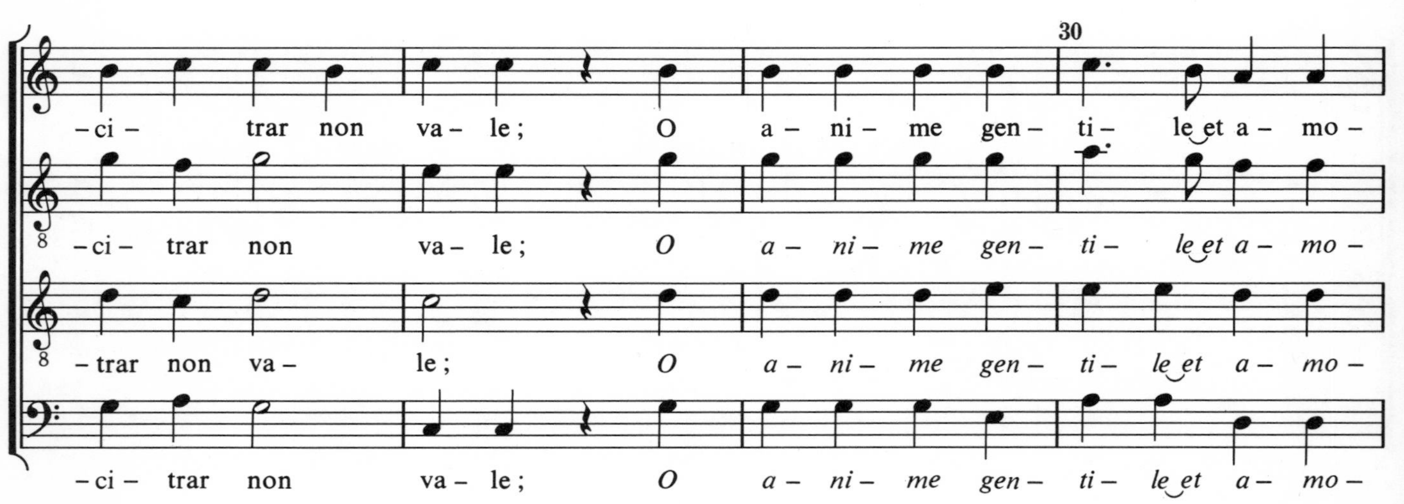
30
– ci – trar non va – le; O a – ni – me gen – ti – le et a – mo –
– ci – trar non va – le; O a – ni – me gen – ti – le et a – mo –
– trar non va – le; O a – ni – me gen – ti – le et a – mo –
– ci – trar non va – le; O a – ni – me gen – ti – le et a – mo –

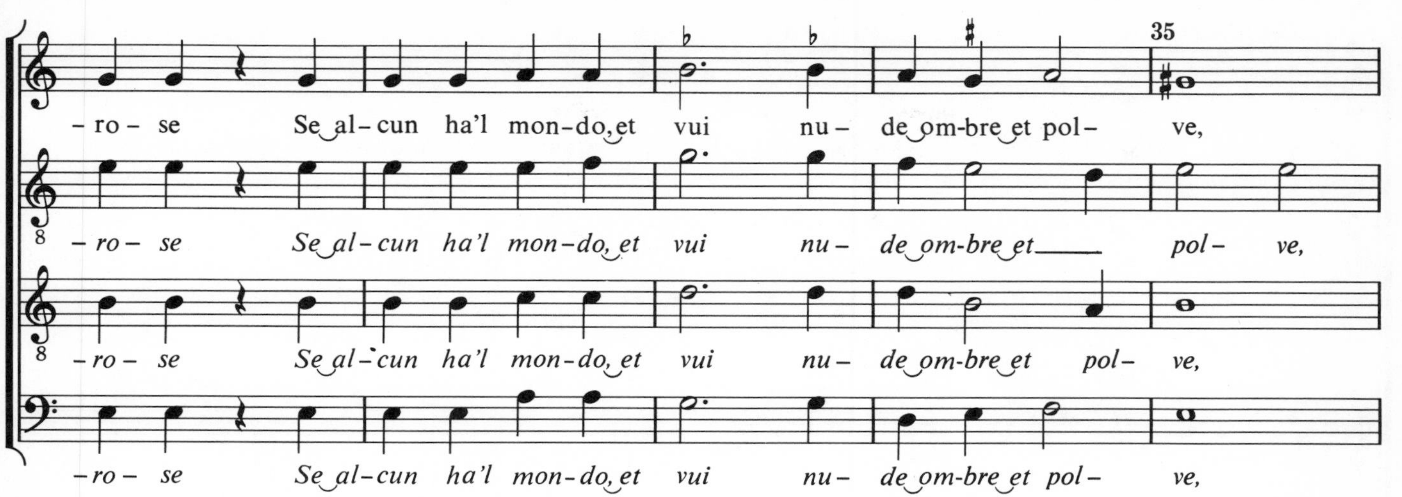
35
-ro- se Se al-cun ha'l mon-do, et vui nu- de om-bre et pol- ve,
-ro- se Se al-cun ha'l mon-do, et vui nu- de om-bre et pol- ve,
-ro- se Se al-cun ha'l mon-do, et vui nu- de om-bre et pol- ve,
-ro- se Se al-cun ha'l mon-do, et vui nu- de om-bre et pol- ve,

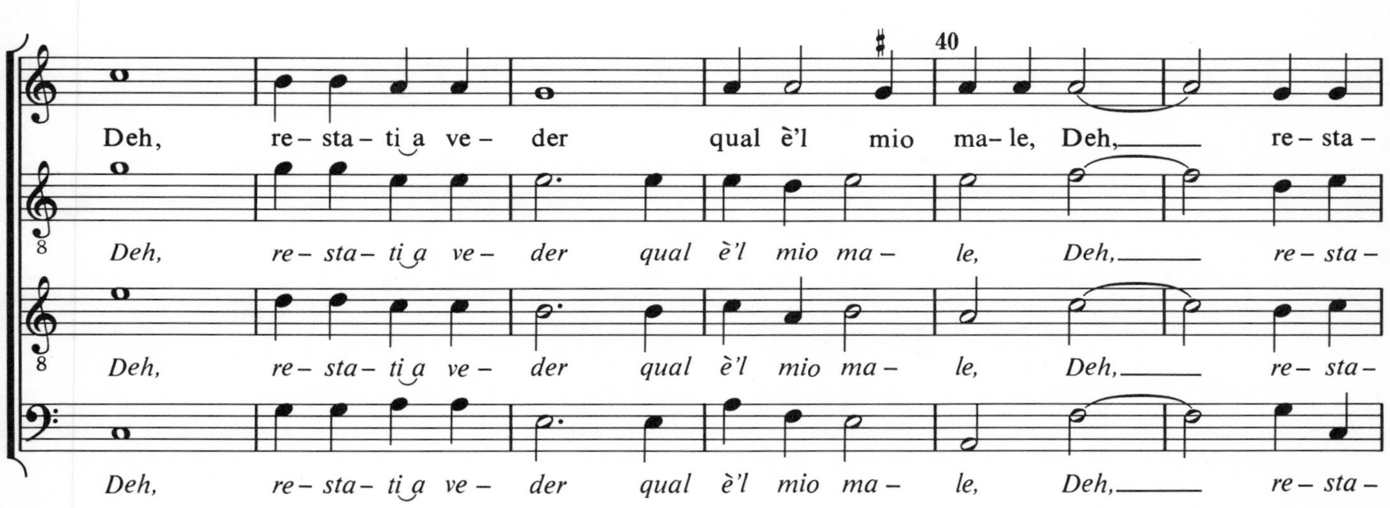
40
Deh, re- sta- ti a ve- der qual è'l mio ma- le, Deh, re- sta-
Deh, re- sta- ti a ve- der qual è'l mio ma- le, Deh, re- sta-
Deh, re- sta- ti a ve- der qual è'l mio ma- le, Deh, re- sta-
Deh, re- sta- ti a ve- der qual è'l mio ma- le, Deh, re- sta-

45
-ti a ve- der qual è'l mio ma- - le, Deh, re- sta- ti a ve- der
-ti a ve- der qual è'l mio ma- - le, Deh, re- sta- ti a ve- der
-ti a ve- der qual è'l mio ma- - le, Deh, re- sta- ti a ve- der
-ti a ve- der qual è'l mio ma- - le, Deh, re- sta- ti a ve- der

[5.] Piangea la donna mia

Anonymous

M[archetto] C[ara]

5
E___ su- spi-ra- va in- ve- ce de pa-ro- - le.
E-ra-ve il sol pre-
La pio-ga e'l ven-to al-
10
-sen- te Et per pie- tà di noi, pian- se e- gli an- cho-
-ho- ra Ba- gno-mi el cal- do e spes- so è il so- le ar- den-
15
-ra, Et su- spi- ran-do an- dò ver- so oc- ci- den- te;
-te; Poi ria-sciu-gom-mi et ri- scal-do in po- c'ho- ra.

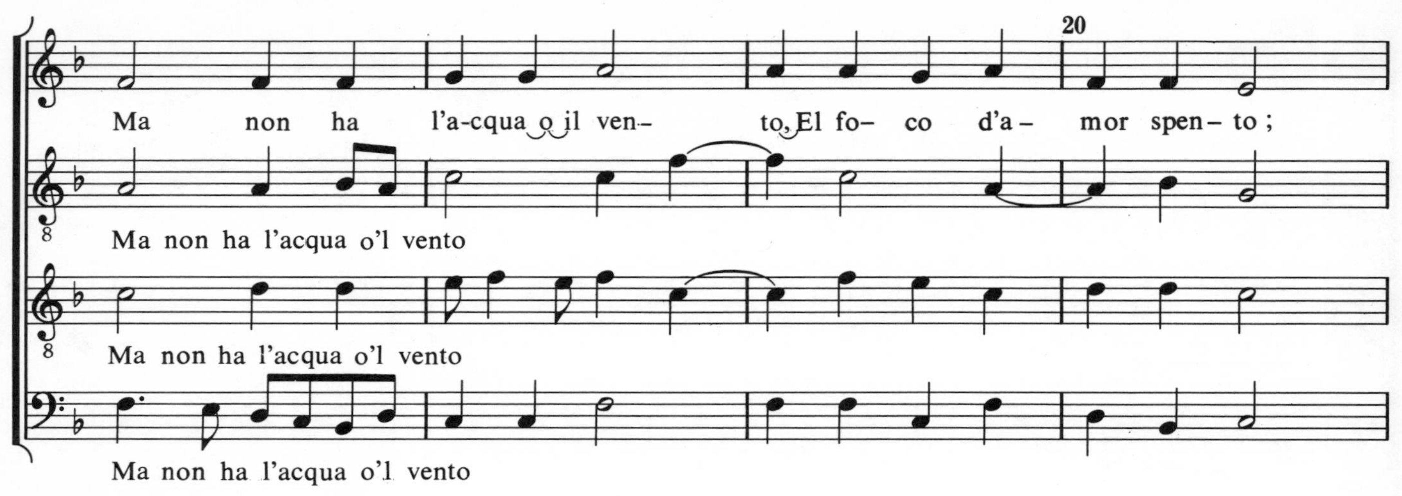
20
Ma non ha l'a-cqua o il ven– to, El fo– co d'a– mor spen– to ;
Ma non ha l'acqua o'l vento
Ma non ha l'acqua o'l vento
Ma non ha l'acqua o'l vento

Nè le la-chry-me mie m'a– sciu–ga il so– – le, Nè le la–

25
–chry–me mie m'a – sciu– ga il so – le, Nè le la-chry-me mie m'a- sciu-

[6.] Perchè quel che mi trasse

Petrarch

Sebastian Festa

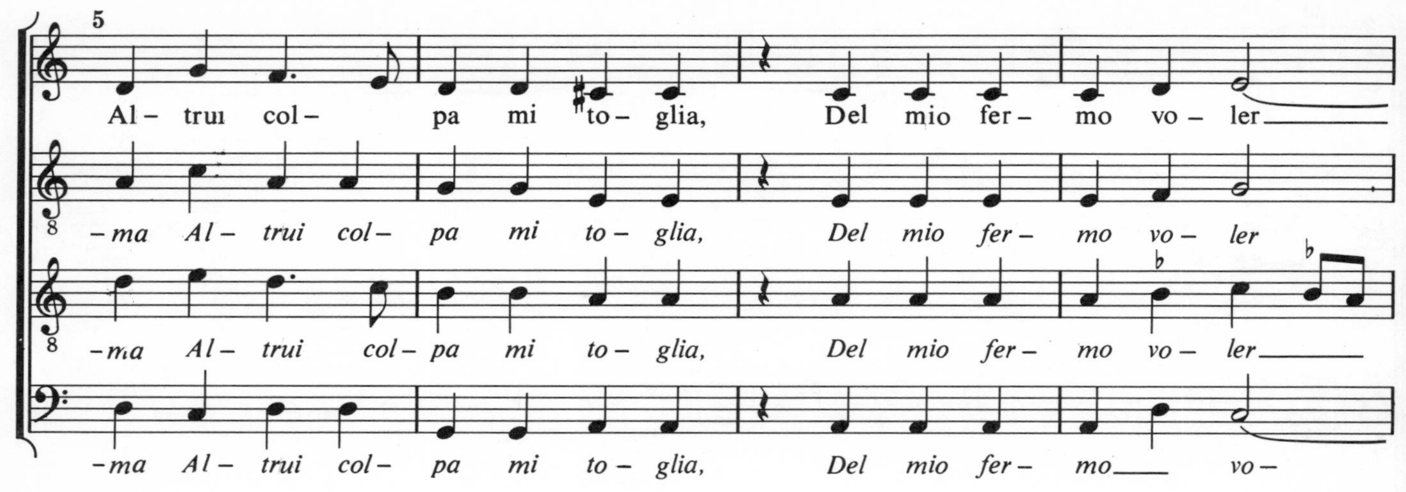
5
Al – trui col – pa mi to – glia, Del mio fer – mo vo – ler
–ma Al – trui col – pa mi to – glia, Del mio fer – mo vo – ler
–ma Al – trui col – pa mi to – glia, Del mio fer – mo vo – ler
–ma Al – trui col – pa mi to – glia, Del mio fer – mo vo –

10
già non mi svo – glia. Tra le chiu – me de l'or
E da be – gli oc-chi mos –
già non mi svo – glia. Tra le chiu – me de l'or
E da be – gli oc-chi mos –
già non mi svo – glia. Tra le chiu – me de l'or
E da be – gli oc-chi mos –
– ler già non mi svo – glia. Tra le chiu – me de l'or
E da be – gli oc-chi mos –

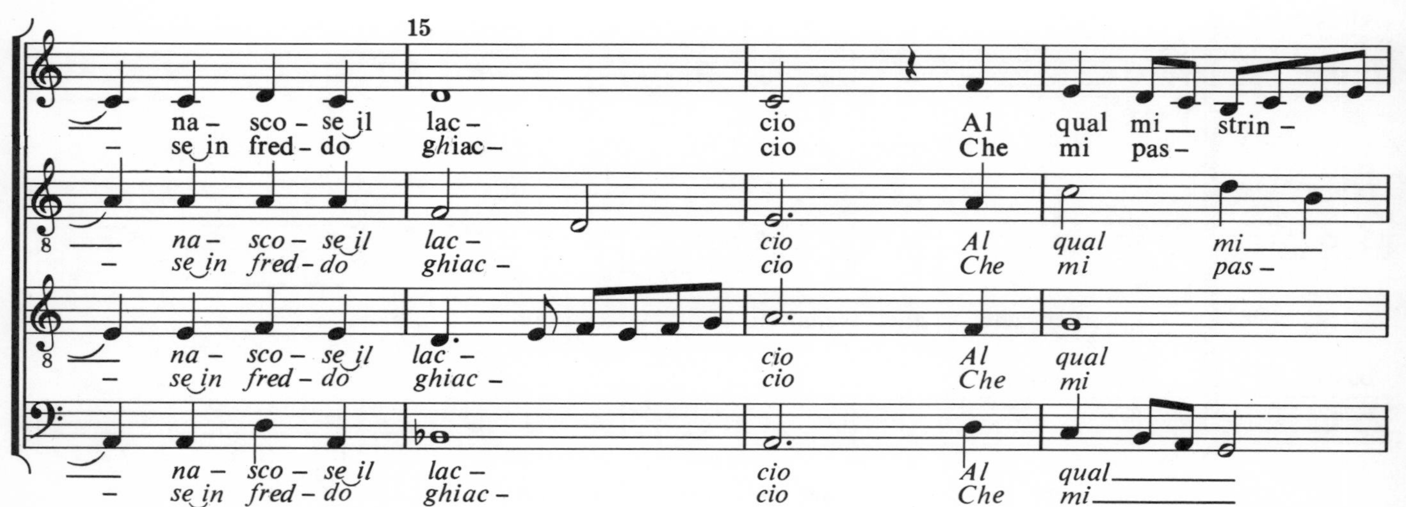
15
na – sco – se il lac – cio Al qual mi strin –
– se in fred – do ghiac – cio Che mi pas –
na – sco – se il lac – cio Al qual mi
– se in fred – do ghiac – cio Che mi pas –
na – sco – se il lac – cio Al qual
– se in fred – do ghiac – cio Che mi
na – sco – se il lac – cio Al qual
– se in fred – do ghiac – cio Che mi

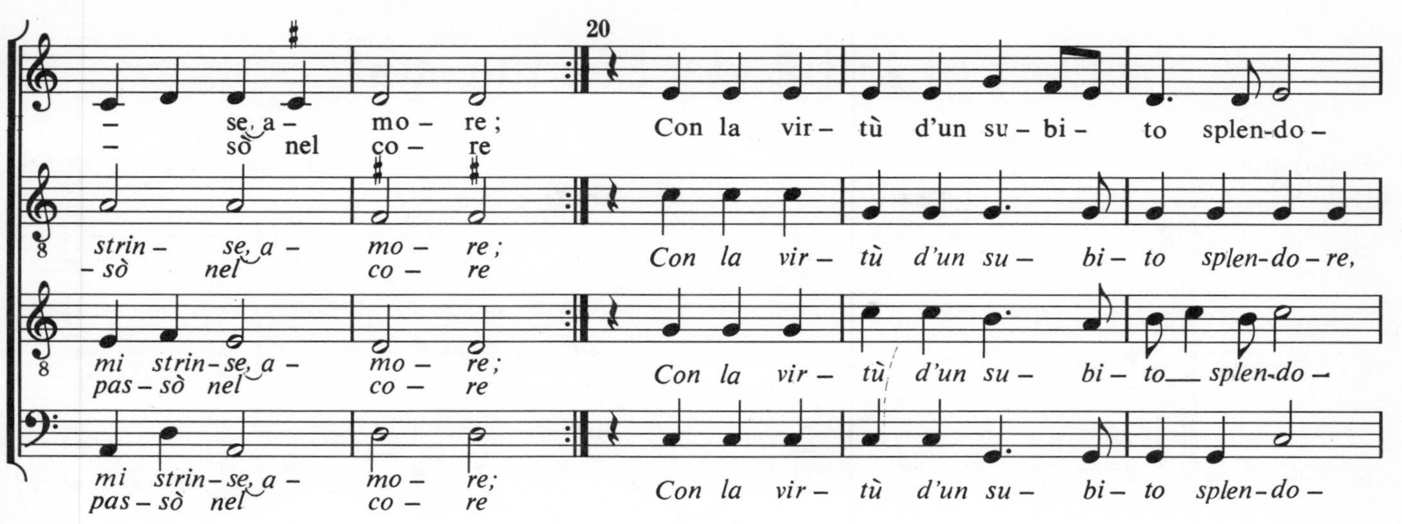
20
– se, a – mo – re ; Con la vir – tù d'un su – bi – to splen-do –
– sò nel co – re
strin – se, a – mo – re ; Con la vir – tù d'un su – bi – to splen-do – re,
– sò nel co – re
mi strin-se, a – mo – re ; Con la vir – tù d'un su – bi – to splen-do –
pas – sò nel co – re
mi strin – se, a – mo – re; Con la vir – tù d'un su – bi – to splen-do –
pas – sò nel co – re

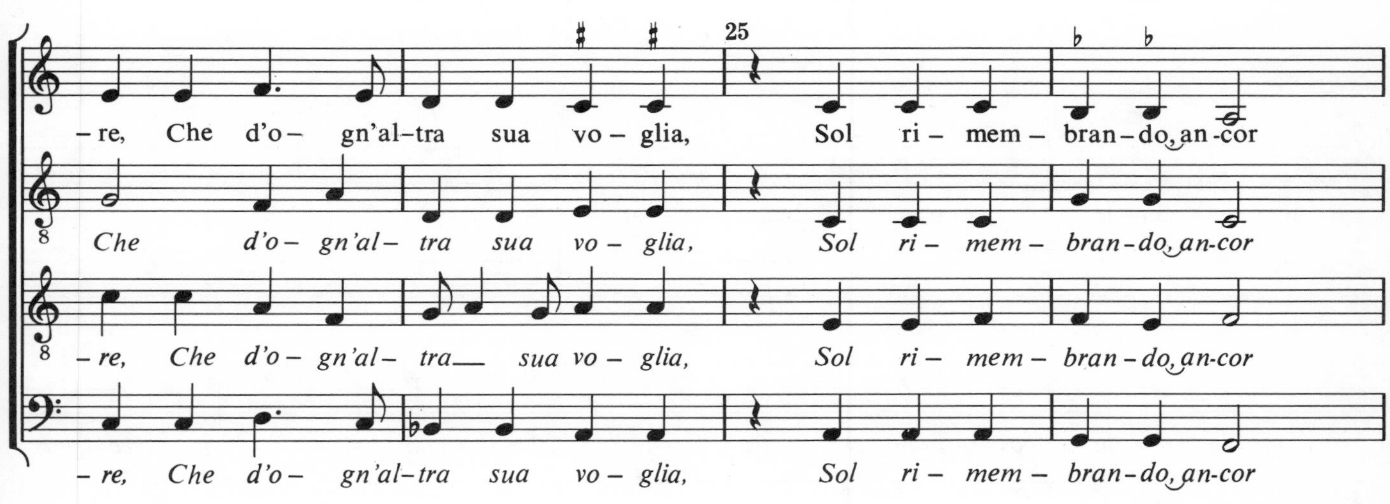
25
– re, Che d'o – gn'al–tra sua vo – glia, Sol ri – mem – bran – do, an -cor
Che d'o – gn'al – tra sua vo – glia, Sol ri – mem – bran-do, an-cor
– re, Che d'o – gn'al – tra sua vo – glia, Sol ri – mem – bran – do, an-cor
– re, Che d'o – gn'al–tra sua vo – glia, Sol ri – mem – bran-do, an-cor

30
l'a – ni – ma spo – glia, l'a – ni – ma spo – glia.
l'a – ni – ma spo – glia, l'a – ni – ma spo – glia.
l'a – ni – ma spo – glia, l'a – ni – ma spo– glia.
l'a – ni – ma spo – glia, l'a – ni – ma spo – glia.

[7.] Dillà da l'acqua sta

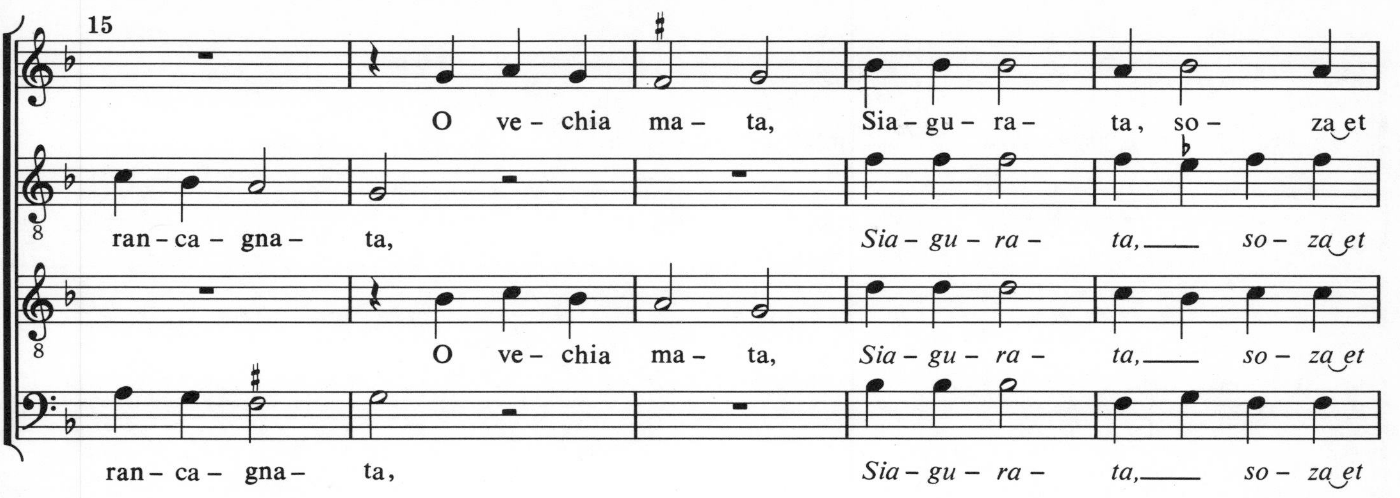
15
O ve – chia ma – ta, Sia – gu – ra – ta, so – za et
ran – ca – gna – ta, Sia – gu – ra – ta, so – za et
O ve – chia ma – ta, Sia – gu – ra – ta, so – za et
ran – ca – gna – ta, Sia – gu – ra – ta, so – za et

20
spor – cha, Vi – so d'or – cha,
spor – cha, rab – bi – o – – sa,
spor – cha, Vi – so d'or – cha,
spor – cha, Vi – so d'or – cha, rab – bi – o – sa,

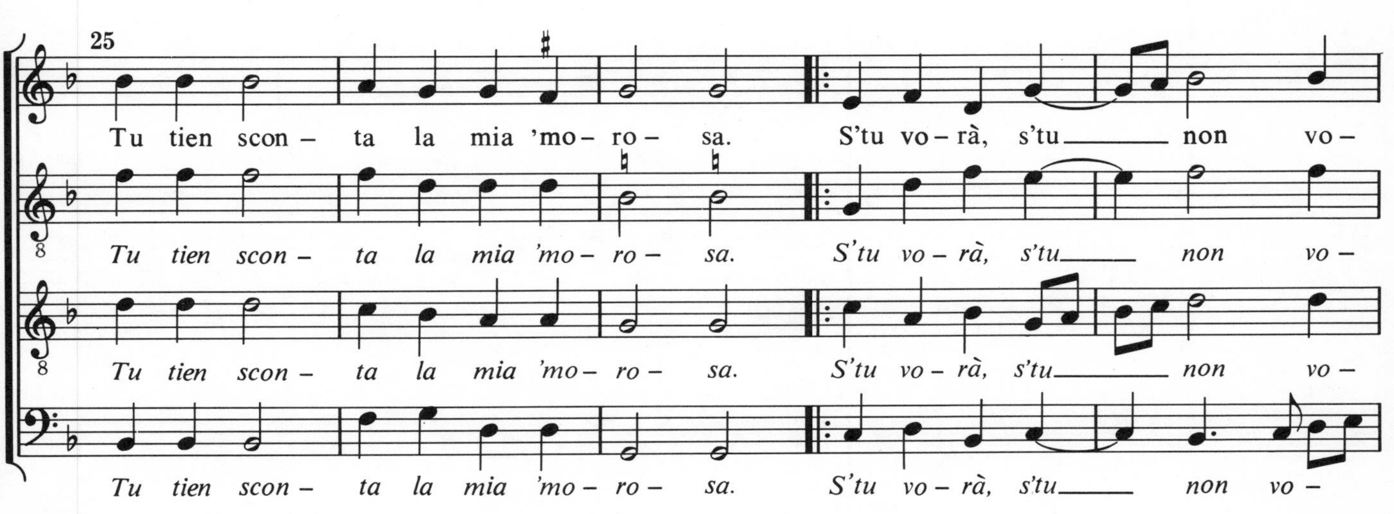
25
Tu tien scon – ta la mia 'mo – ro – sa. S'tu vo – rà, s'tu non vo –
Tu tien scon – ta la mia 'mo – ro – sa. S'tu vo – rà, s'tu non vo –
Tu tien scon – ta la mia 'mo – ro – sa. S'tu vo – rà, s'tu non vo –
Tu tien scon – ta la mia 'mo – ro – sa. S'tu vo – rà, s'tu non vo –

[8.] Non al suo amante

Petrarch

[Sebastian Festa]

5
– do per tal ven – tu – ra tut – ta i – gnu – – da La
– do per tal ven – tu – ra tut – ta i – gnu – da La
– do per tal ven – tu – ra tut – ta i – gnu – da La
– do per tal ven – tu – ra tut – ta i – gnu – da La

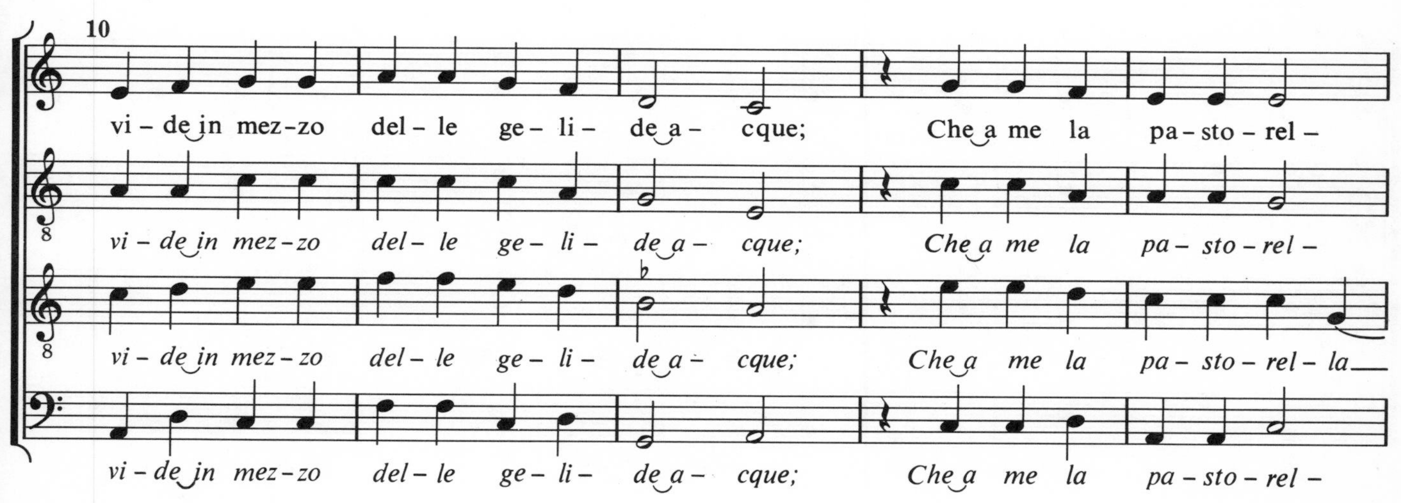
10
vi – de in mez-zo del – le ge – li – de a – cque; Che a me la pa – sto – rel –
vi – de in mez – zo del – le ge – li – de a – cque; Che a me la pa – sto – rel –
vi – de in mez – zo del – le ge – li – de a – cque; Che a me la pa – sto – rel – la
vi – de in mez – zo del – le ge – li – de a – cque; Che a me la pa – sto – rel –

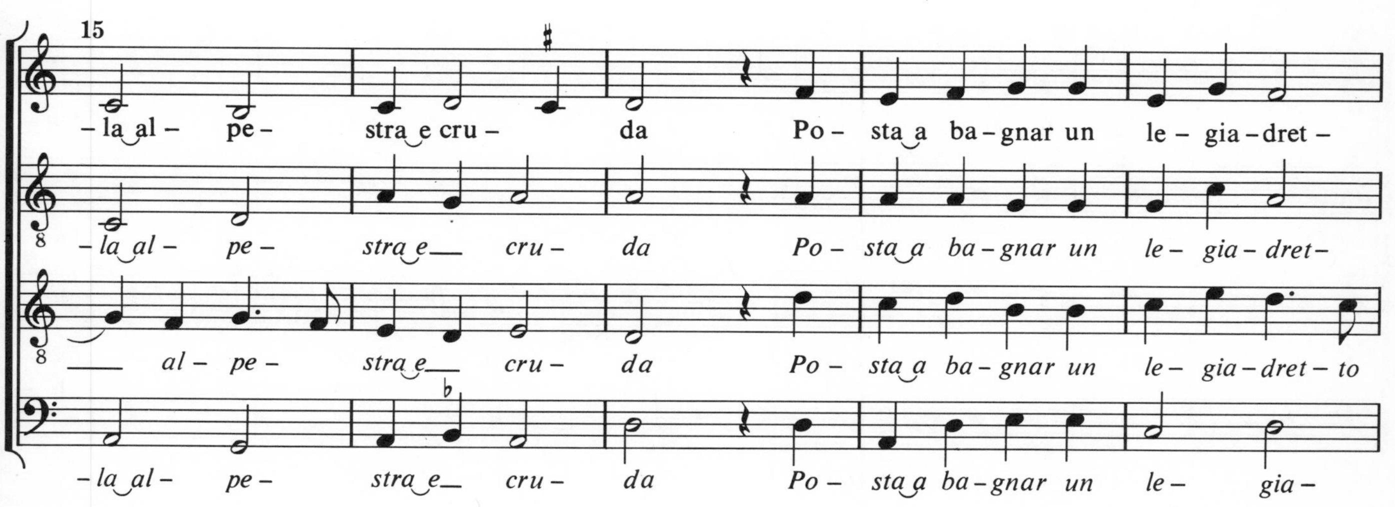
15
– la al – pe – stra e cru – da Po – sta a ba – gnar un le – gia – dret –
– la al – pe – stra e cru – da Po – sta a ba – gnar un le – gia – dret –
al – pe – stra e cru – da Po – sta a ba – gnar un le – gia – dret – to
– la al – pe – stra e cru – da Po – sta a ba – gnar un le – gia –

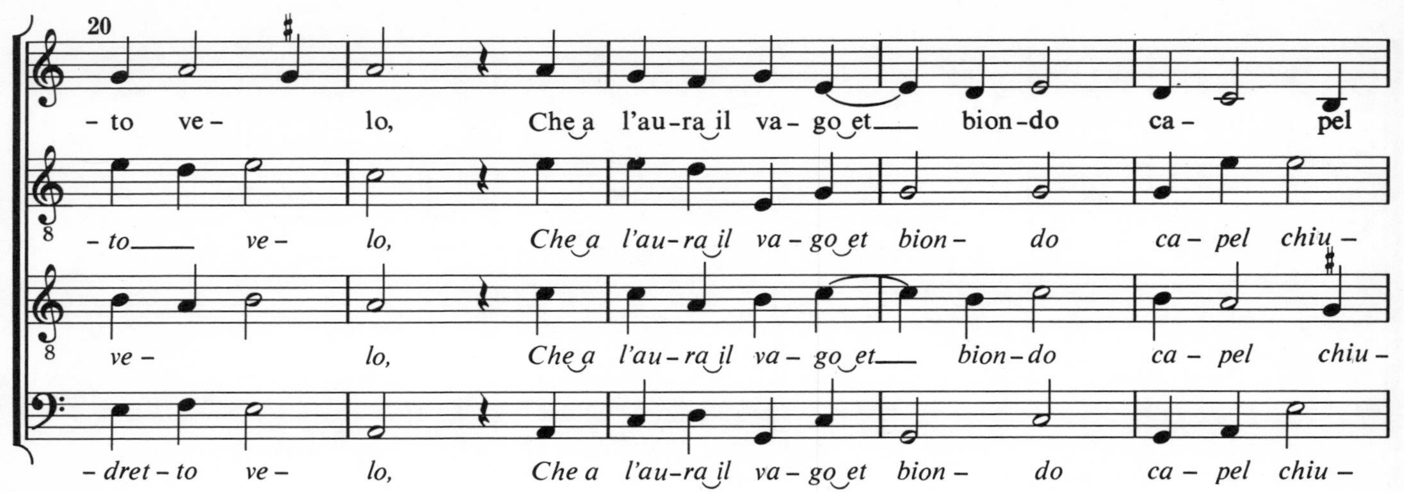
20
– to ve – lo, Che a l'au-ra il va-go et bion-do ca – pel
– to ve – lo, Che a l'au-ra il va-go et bion- do ca-pel chiu –
ve – lo, Che a l'au-ra il va-go et bion-do ca – pel chiu –
– dret – to ve – lo, Che a l'au-ra il va-go et bion – do ca – pel chiu –

25
chiu-da; Tal che mi fe – ce hor quan – do e-gli ar-de il cie –
– da; Tal che – mi fe – ce hor quan – do e – gli ar-de il cie –
– da; Tal che – mi fe – ce hor quan – do e – gli ar-de il cie –
– da; Tal che – mi fe – ce hor quan-do e – gli ar – de il cie –

30
– lo, Tut – to trem–mar d'un a – mo – ro – so gie – lo, Tut –
– lo, Tut – to trem–mar d'un a – mo – ro – so gie – lo, Tut –
– lo, Tut – to trem–mar d'un a – mo – ro – so gie – lo, Tut –
– lo, Tut – to trem–mar d'un a – mo – ro – so gie – lo, Tut –

[9.] Del mio sì grande

S. dall' Aquila M[archetto] C[ara]

[10.] Poichè in van

Anonymous

M[archetto] C[ara]

spar-si al ven– to, Da qui in-nan– ti più con– ten– to, Can– te-rò
sen– za ver– – go– gna: "Ve– gnan-do da Bo– lo– gna,
La scar– pa mi fa ma– le; Tan– da– ron– da– rin– dun– da."

[11.] Un cavalier de Spagna

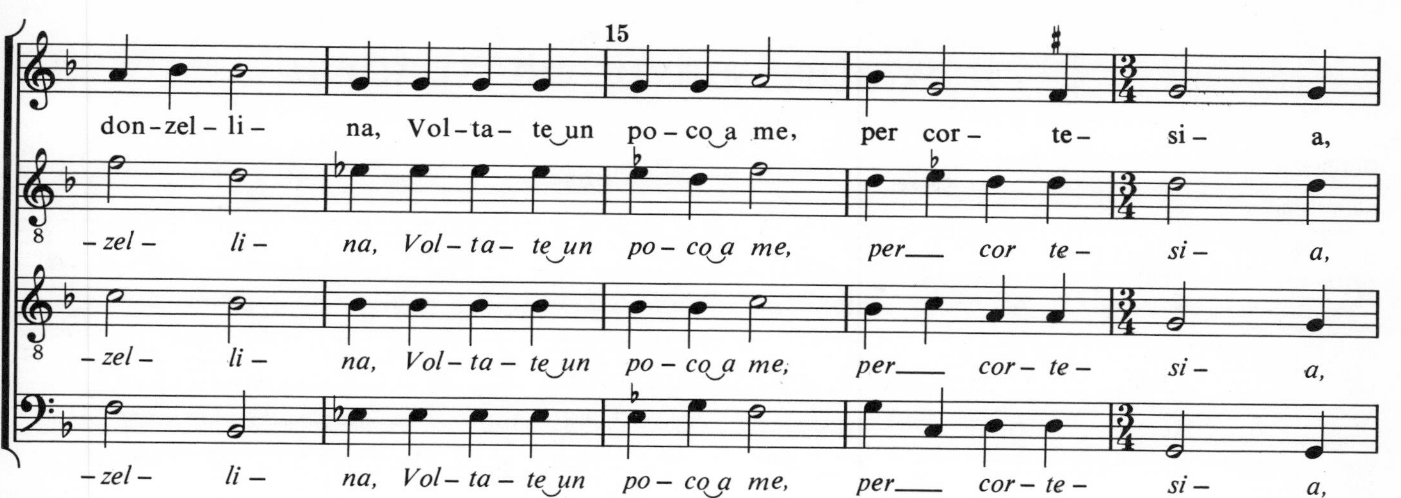
15
don-zel-li- na, Vol-ta- te un po-co a me, per cor- te- si- a,
-zel- li- na, Vol-ta- te un po-co a me, per cor te- si- a,
-zel- li- na, Vol-ta- te un po-co a me, per cor-te- si- a,
-zel- li- na, Vol-ta- te un po-co a me, per cor-te- si- a,

20
Dol-ce spe- ran- za mi- a, Che mo- ro per tuo a-
Dol- ce spe- ran- za mi- a, Che mo- ro per tuo a-
Dol- ce spe- ran- za mi- a, Che mo- ro per tuo a-
Dol- ce spe- ran- za mi- a, Che mo- ro per tuo a-

25
- mor; Bel- la fan- ti- na, i' t'ho do- na- to el cor."
- mor; Bel- la fan- ti- na, i' t'ho do- na- to el cor."
- mor; Bel- la fan- ti- na, i' t'ho do- na- to el cor."
- mor; Bel- la fan- ti- na, i' t'ho do- na- to el cor."

[12.] Amor, se voi ch'io torni

15
vin – cer pri – – a. Il mio a-ma – to the-so – ro in
vin – cer pri – – a. Il mio a-ma – to the – so – ro in
– ti vin – cer pri – a. Il mio a-ma – to the – so – ro in
vin – cer pri – – a. Il mio a-ma – to the – so – ro in

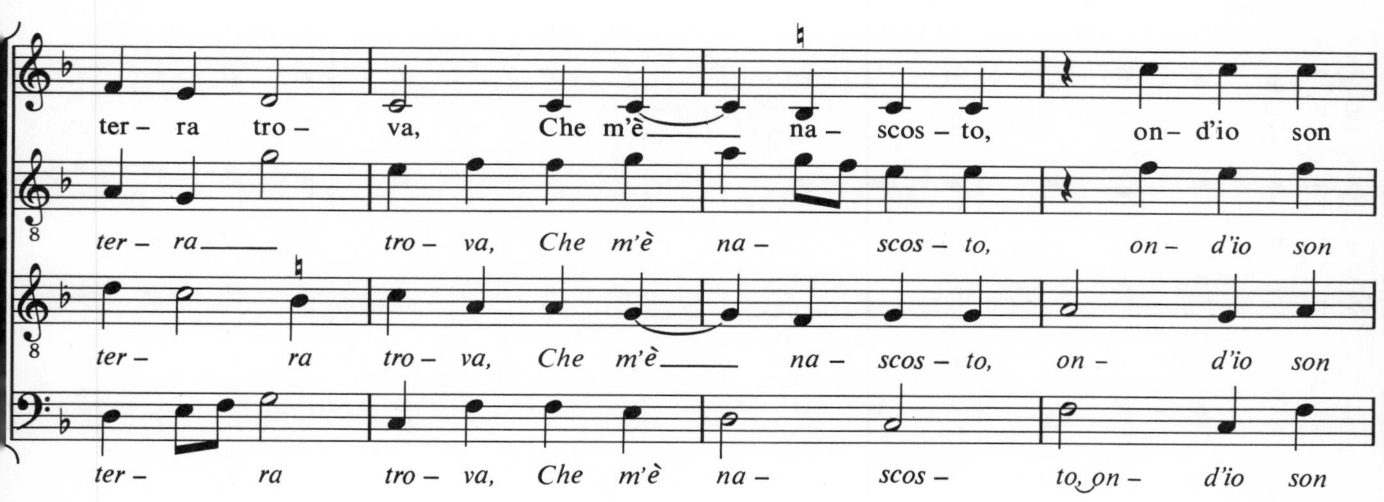
ter – ra tro – va, Che m'è na – scos – to, on – d'io son
ter – ra tro – va, Che m'è na – scos – to, on – d'io son
ter – ra tro – va, Che m'è na – scos – to, on – d'io son
ter – ra tro – va, Che m'è na – scos – to, on – d'io son

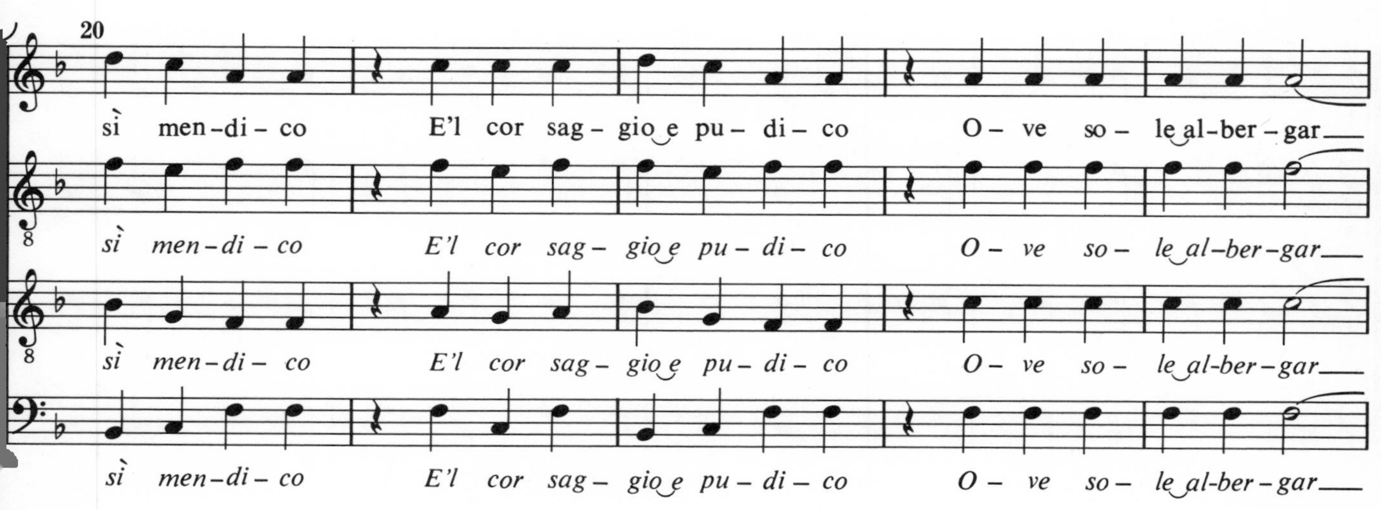
20
sì men-di – co E'l cor sag – gio e pu – di – co O – ve so – le al-ber – gar
sì men-di – co E'l cor sag – gio e pu – di – co O – ve so – le al-ber-gar
sì men-di – co E'l cor sag – gio e pu – di – co O – ve so – le al-ber-gar
sì men-di – co E'l cor sag – gio e pu – di – co O – ve so – le al-ber-gar

25
30
la vi – – ta mi – a: E s'e – gli è ver che tua po – ten – – za si – a
la vi – ta mi – a: E s'e – gli è ver che tua po – ten – za si – a
la vi – ta mi – a: E s'e – gli è ver che tua po – ten – za si – a
la vi – ta mi – a: E s'e – gli è ver che tua po – ten – za si – a

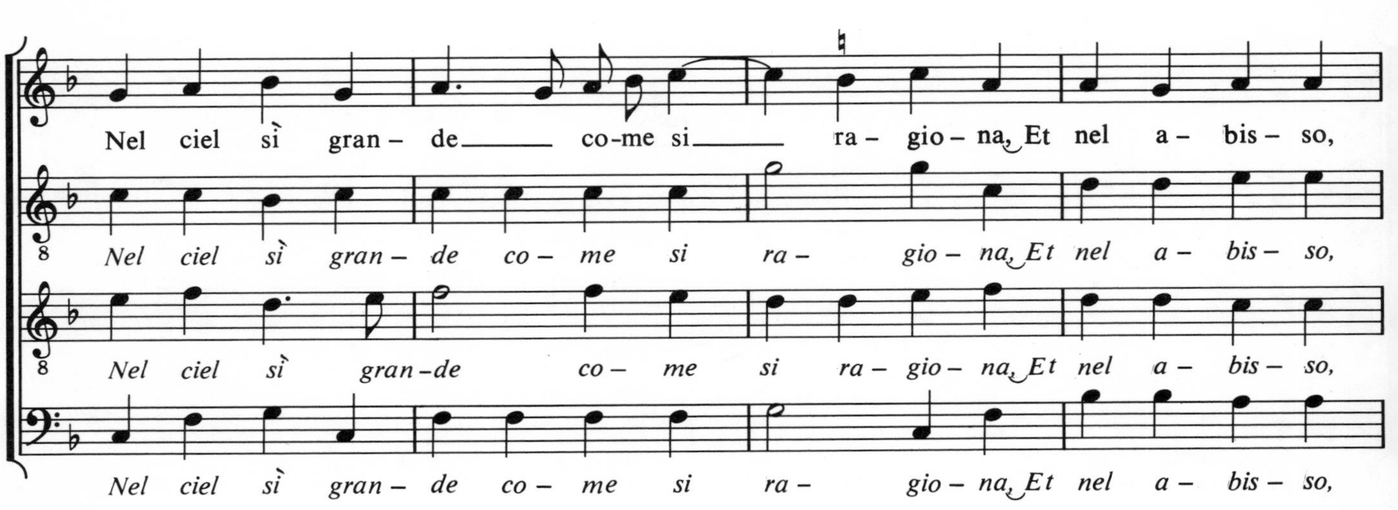
Nel ciel sì gran – de co – me si ra – gio – na, Et nel a – bis – so,
Nel ciel sì gran – de co – me si ra – gio – na, Et nel a – bis – so,
Nel ciel sì gran – de co – me si ra – gio – na, Et nel a – bis – so,
Nel ciel sì gran – de co – me si ra – gio – na, Et nel a – bis – so,

35
per – chè qui fra no – i Quel che tu va – li e po – i
per – chè qui fra no – i Quel che tu va – – li e po – i
per – chè qui fra no – i Quel che tu va – li e po – i
per – chè qui fra no – i Quel che tu va – – li e po – i

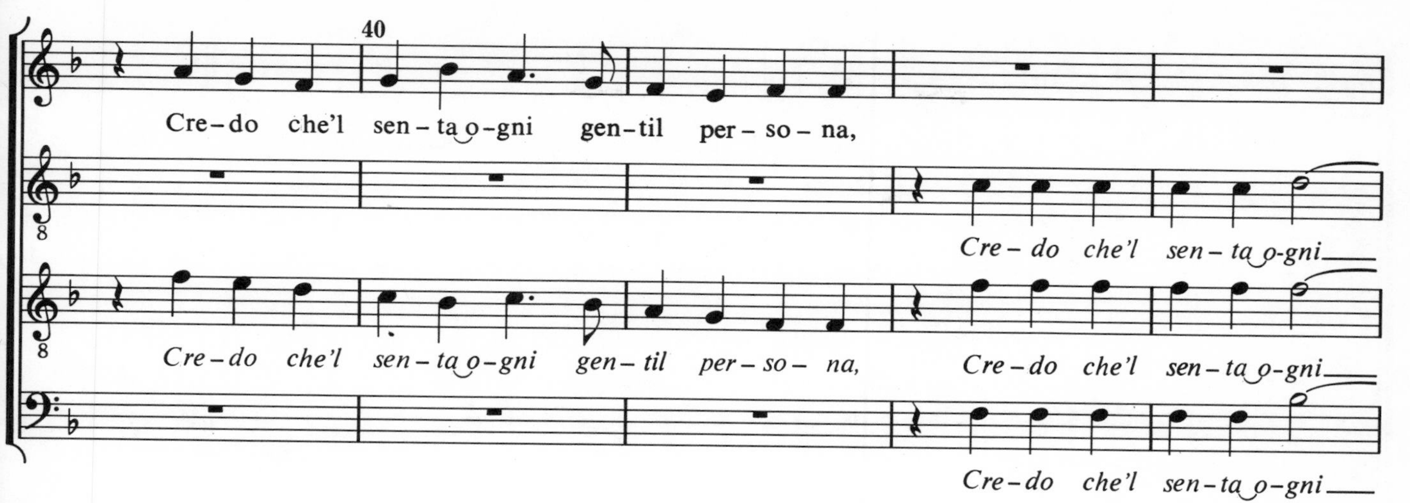
40
Cre–do che'l sen–ta o–gni gen–til per–so–na,
Cre–do che'l sen–ta o–gni
Cre–do che'l sen–ta o–gni gen–til per–so–na, Cre–do che'l sen–ta o–gni
Cre–do che'l sen–ta o–gni

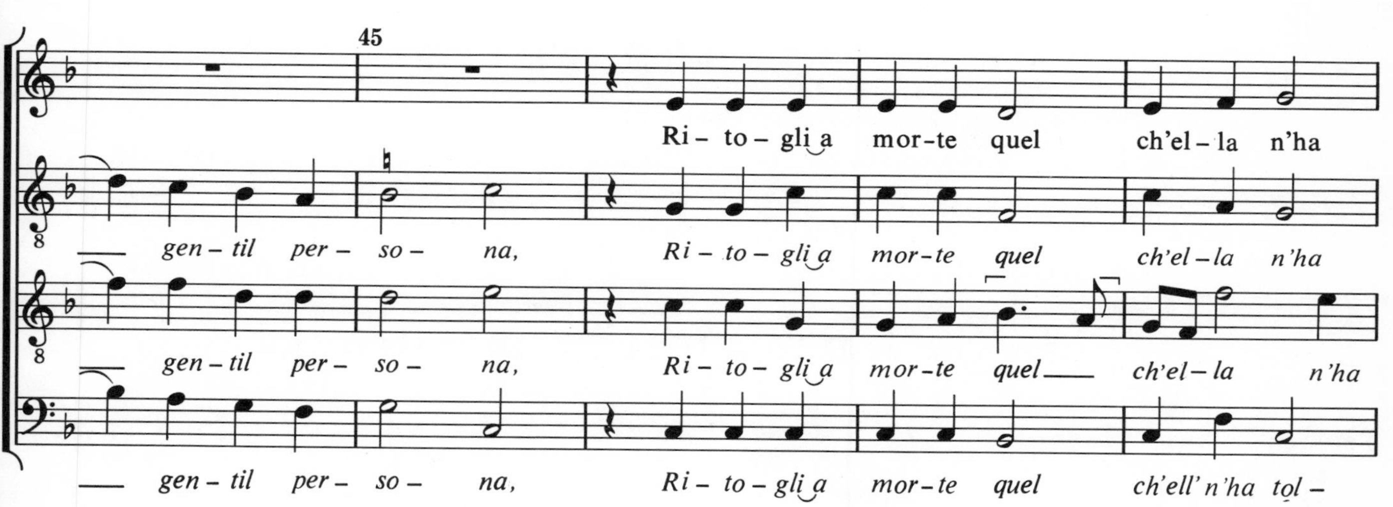
45
Ri–to–gli a mor–te quel ch'el–la n'ha
gen–til per–so–na, Ri–to–gli a mor–te quel ch'el–la n'ha
gen–til per–so–na, Ri–to–gli a mor–te quel ch'el–la n'ha
gen–til per–so–na, Ri–to–gli a mor–te quel ch'ell'n'ha tol–

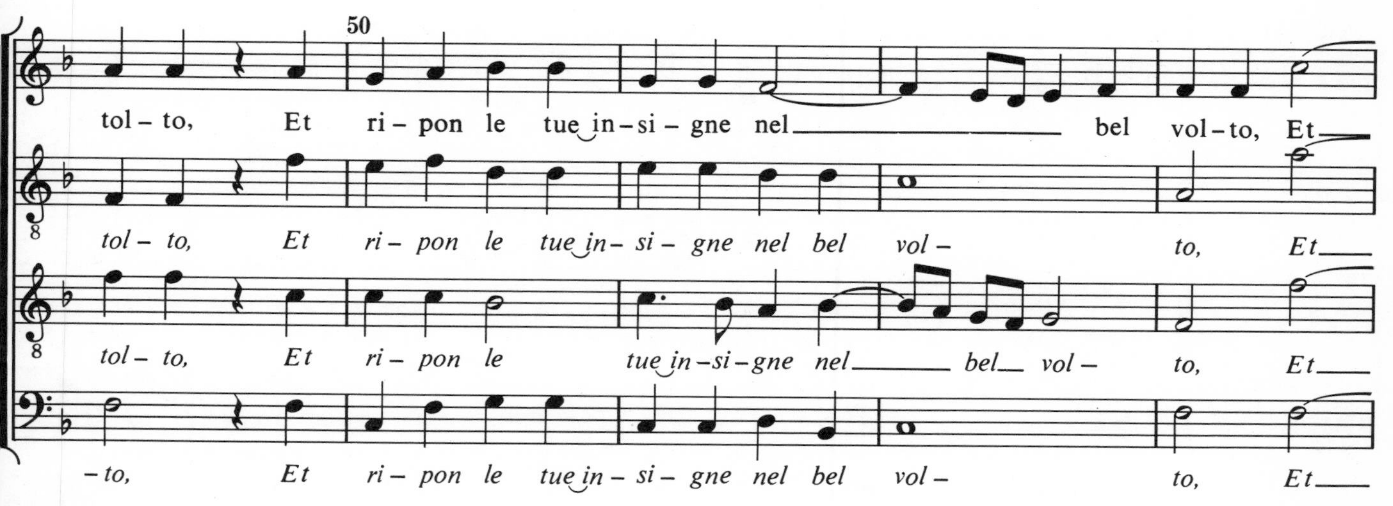
50
tol–to, Et ri–pon le tue in–si–gne nel bel vol–to, Et
tol–to, Et ri–pon le tue in–si–gne nel bel vol– to, Et
tol–to, Et ri–pon le tue in–si–gne nel bel vol– to, Et
–to, Et ri–pon le tue in–si–gne nel bel vol– to, Et

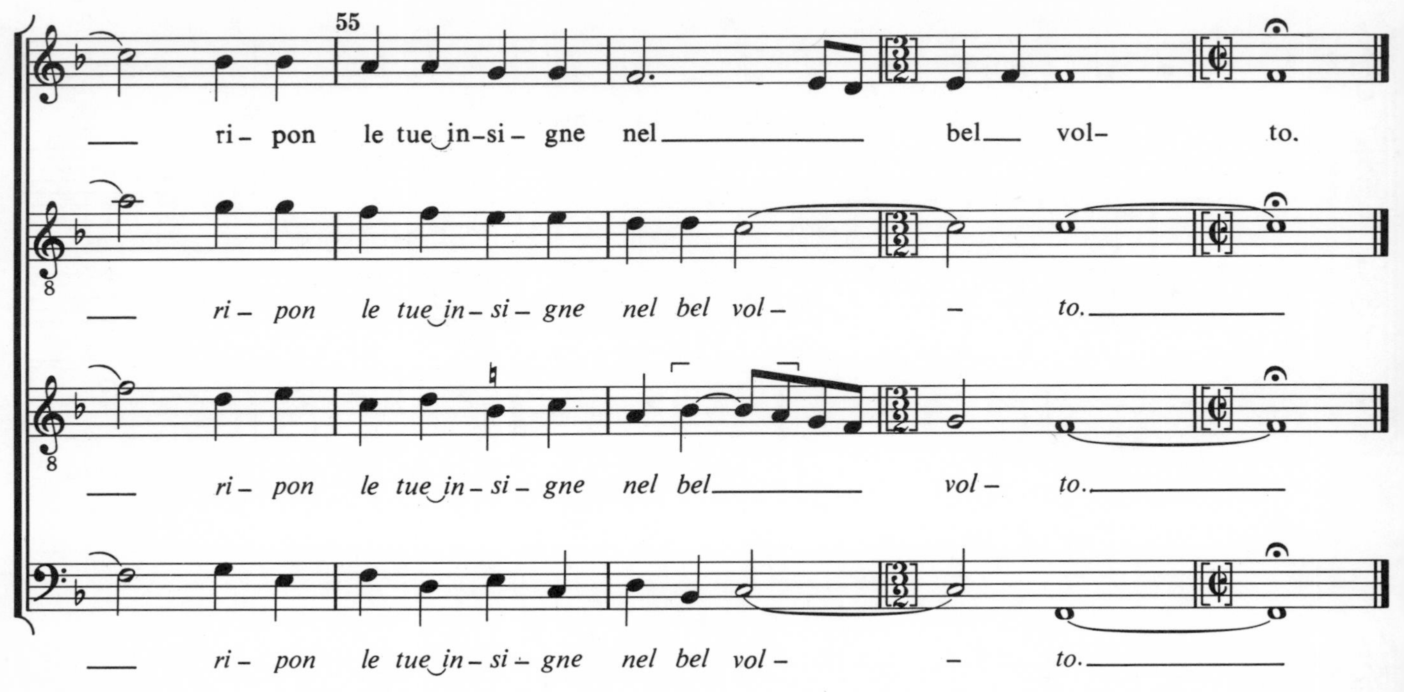

[13.] Se 'l pensier che mi strugge

Petrarch

Sebastian Festa

Co– m'è pun– gen– te͜ e sal– do Co– sì ve–
Ch'a – vria par – te del cal– do, Et de– ste–
Co– m'è pun– gen– te͜ e sal– do Co– sì ve–
Ch'a –vria par– te del cal– do, Et de– ste–
Co– m'è pun– gen– te͜ e sal– do Co– sì ve–
Ch'a – vria par – te del cal– do, Et de– ste–
– m'è pun– gen– te͜ e sal– do Co– sì ve–
– vria par – te del cal– do, Et de– ste–
–stis–se d'un co– lor con– for– me,
–ria–se͜ a–mor là do– – ve͜ hor dor– me;
Men so– li–
–stis– se d'un co– – lor con– for– me, Men so– li–
–ria – se͜ a–mor là do– ve hor dor– me;
–stis– se d'un co– lor con– for– me, Men so– li–
–ria – se a͜–mor là do– ve͜ hor dor– me;
–stis– se d'un co– lor con– for– me, Men so– li–
–ria – se͜ a–mor là do– – ve͜ hor dor– me;
–ta–rie l'or–me Fo– ran de' miei piè las–si Per cam–pa–gnie͜ e per
–ta–rie l'or–me Fo– ran de' miei piè las–si Per cam–pa–gnie͜ e per
–ta–rie l'or–me Fo– ran de' miei piè las–si Per cam–pa–gnie͜ e per
–ta–rie l'or–me Fo– ran de' miei piè las–si Per cam–pa–gnie͜ e per

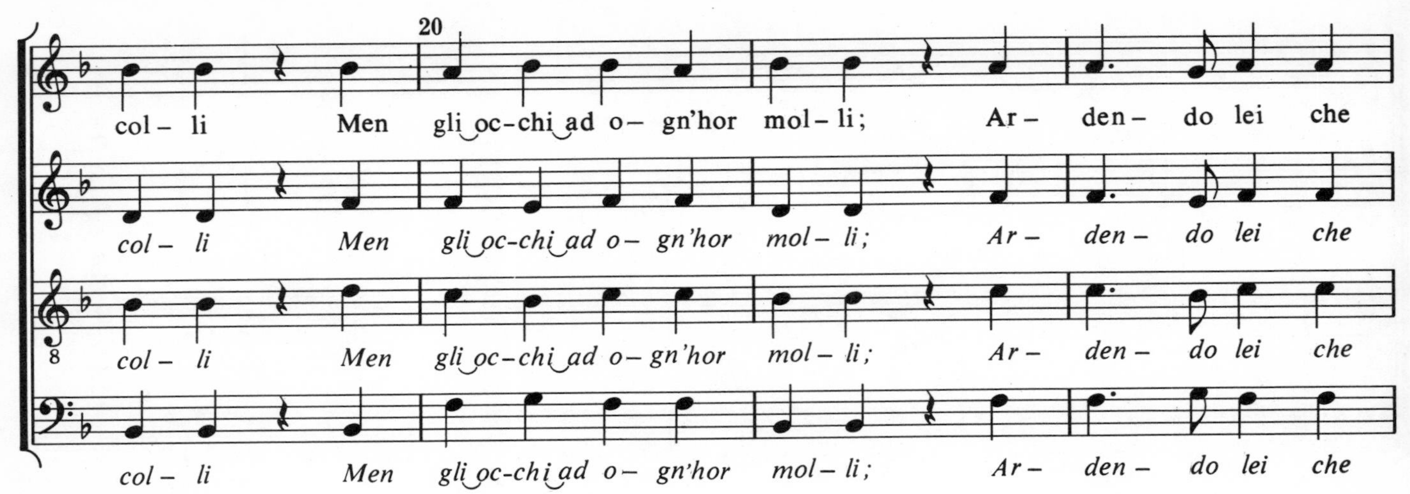
20
col – li Men gli oc-chi ad o– gn'hor mol – li; Ar – den – do lei che
col – li Men gli oc-chi ad o– gn'hor mol – li; Ar – den – do lei che
col – li Men gli oc-chi ad o– gn'hor mol – li; Ar – den – do lei che
col – li Men gli oc-chi ad o– gn'hor mol – li; Ar – den – do lei che

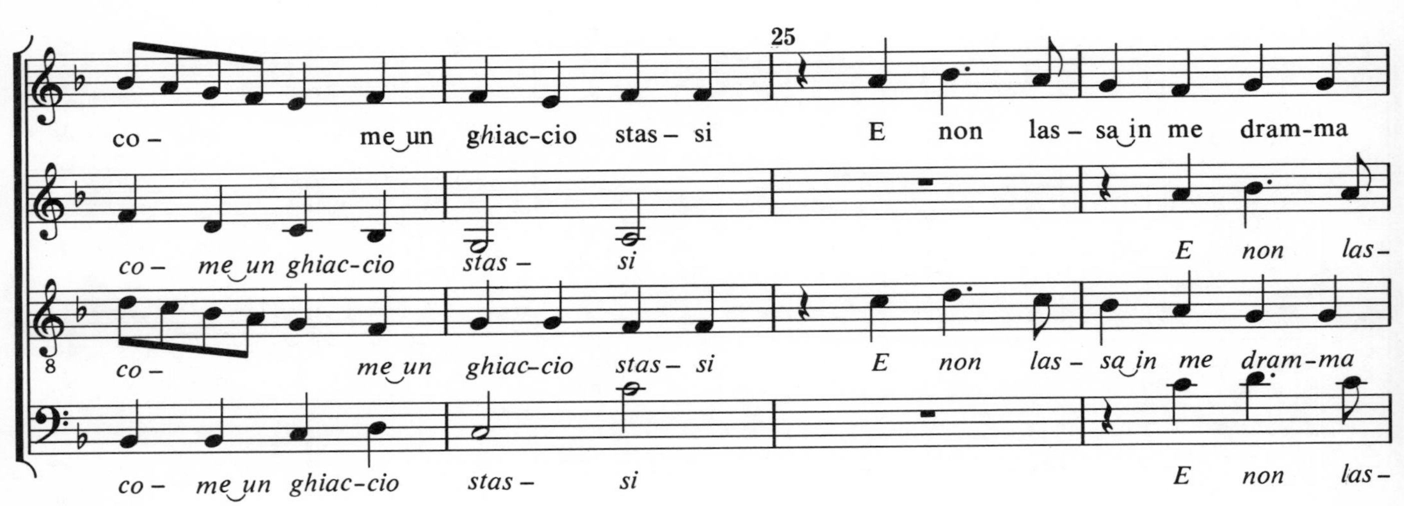
25
co – me un ghiac-cio stas – si E non las – sa in me dram-ma
co – me un ghiac-cio stas – si E non las–
co – me un ghiac-cio stas – si E non las – sa in me dram-ma
co – me un ghiac-cio stas – si E non las–

30
Che non sia fo – co e fiam – ma, E non las –
– sa in me dram–ma Che non sia fo – co e fiam–ma, E non las –
Che non sia fo – co e fiam – ma, E non las –
– sa in me dram–ma Che non sia fo – co e fiam–ma, E non las –

–sa in me dram–ma Che non sia fo– co e fiam–ma, E
–sa in me dram–ma Che non sia fo– co e fiam– ma, E
–sa in me dram–ma Che non sia fo– co e fiam–ma, E
–sa in me dram–ma Che non sia fo– co e fiam–ma, E

35
non las– sa in me dram–ma Che non sia fo– – co e fiam–ma, Che
non las– sa in me dram–ma Che non sia fo– co e fiam– ma, Che
non las– sa in me dram–ma Che non sia fo– – co e fiam–ma, Che
non las– sa in me dram–ma Che non sia fo– co e fiam-ma, Che

40
non sia fo– co e fiam– ma.
non sia fo– co e fiam– ma, Che non sia fo– co e fiam– ma.
non sia fo– co e fiam– ma, Che non sia fo– co e fiam– ma.
non sia fo– co e fiam– ma, Che non sia fo– co e fiam– ma.

[14.] Le son tre fantinelle

Anonymous

M[archetto] C[ara]

[15.] Vrai dieu d'amor

Anonymous

F[rancesco] P[atavino]

10
qui me con– for– te–rà, qui me con–for– te–rà, qui
me con–for– te– rà, qui me con-for– te– rà, qui
qui me con-for– te– rà, qui me, qui
me con–for–te– rà, qui me con–for– te–rà, qui

15
me con-for–te– rà, qui me con–for– te– rà Che'l mio a–mor si
me con–for–te– rà, qui me con– for–te– rà Che'l mio a– mor si
me con–for–te– rà, qui me con– for– te– rà Che'l mio a– mor si
me con–for–te– rà, qui me con– for– te– rà Che'l mio a–mor si

m'à las– sa; Fa-ri–ra fa– ra– ri– rum. Ch'io sum
m'à las– sa; Fa-ri– ra fa– ra– ri– rum. Ch'io sum
m'à las– sa; Fa– ri–ra fa– ra– ri– rum. Ch'io sum
m'à las– sa; Fa-ri– ra fa– ra– ri– rum. Ch'io sum

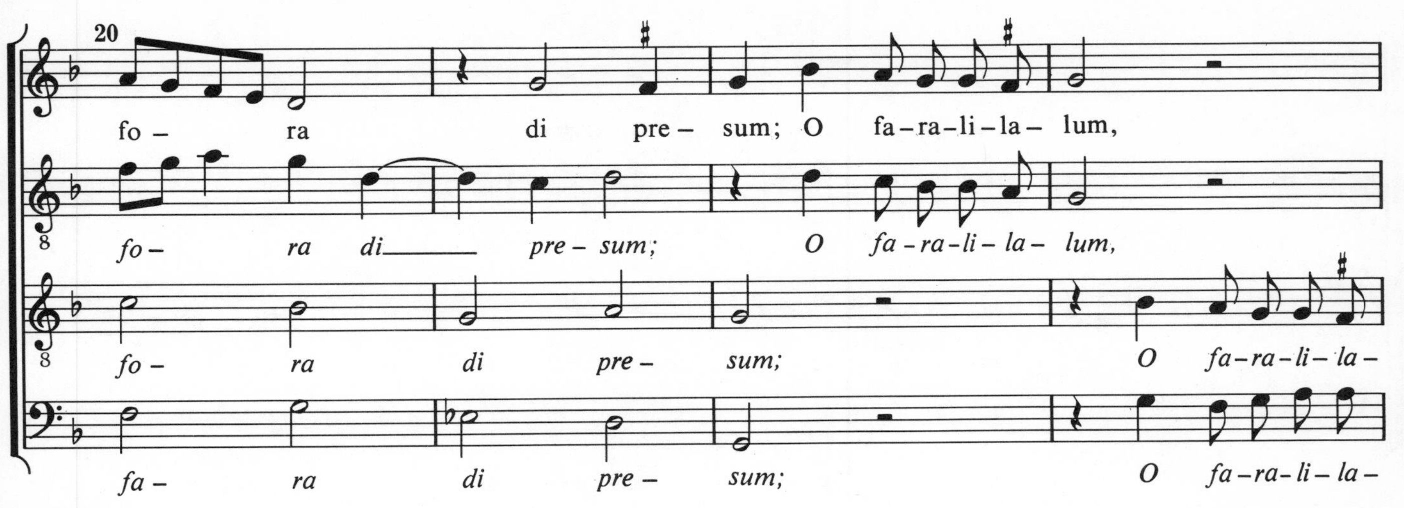
20
fo – ra di pre – sum; O fa–ra–li–la– lum,
fo– ra di pre – sum; O fa–ra–li– la– lum,
fo – ra di pre – sum; O fa–ra–li– la–
fa – ra di pre – sum; O fa–ra–li– la–

25
O fa–ra–li–la– lum, Ch'io sum fo– ra di pre– sum Et vo can–
O fa–ra–li–la– lum, Ch'io sum fo– ra di pre– sum Et vo can–
–lum, O fa–ra–li–la– lum, Ch'io sum fo– ra di pre– sum Et vo can–
–lum, O fa–ra–li–la– lum, Ch'io sum fo– ra di pre– sum Et vo can–

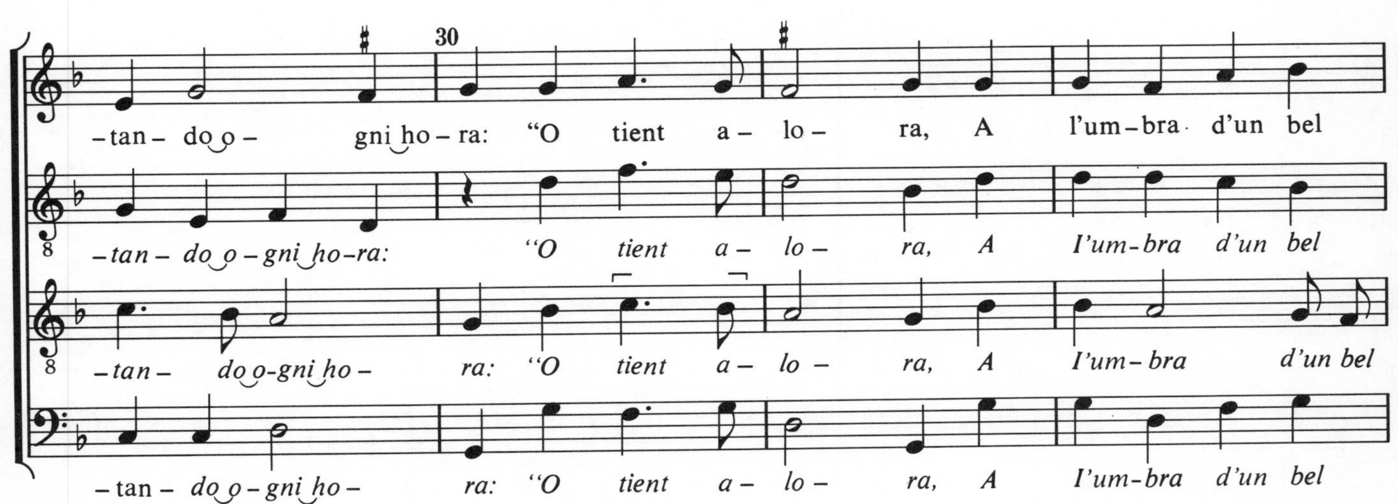
30
–tan– do o– gni ho– ra: "O tient a– lo– ra, A l'um–bra d'un bel
–tan– do o–gni ho–ra: "O tient a– lo– ra, A l'um–bra d'un bel
–tan– do o–gni ho– ra: "O tient a– lo– ra, A l'um–bra d'un bel
–tan– do o–gni ho– ra: "O tient a– lo– ra, A l'um–bra d'un bel

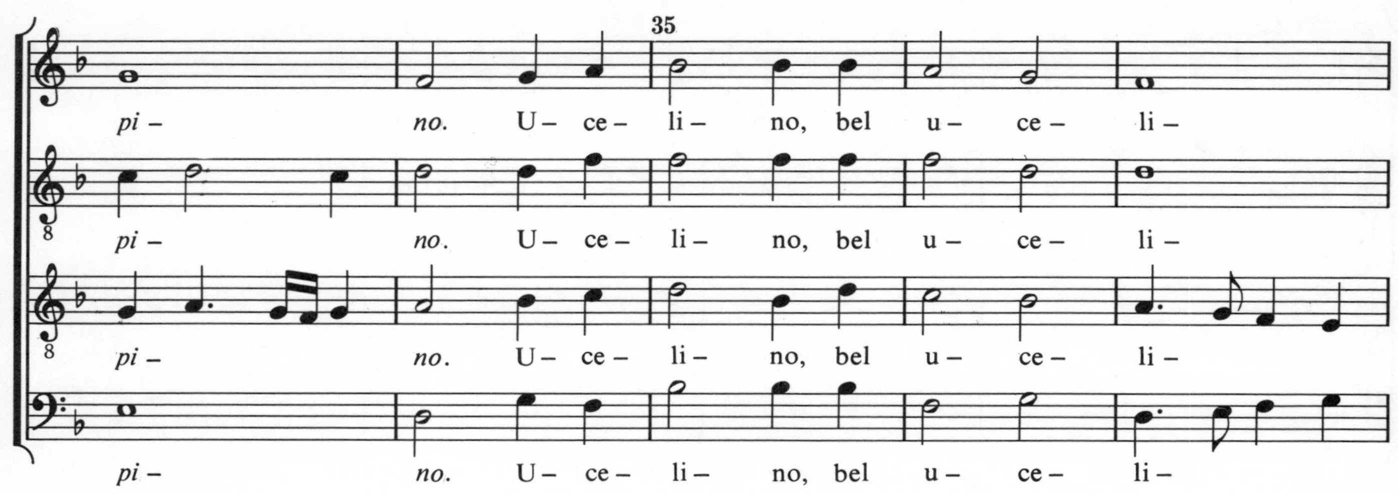
35
pi – no. U– ce – li – no, bel u – ce – li –
pi – no. U– ce – li – no, bel u – ce – li –
pi – no. U– ce – li – no, bel u – ce – li –
pi – no. U– ce – li – no, bel u – ce – li –

40
– no U– ce – li – no, bel u – ce – li – no, Co – me
– no, U – ce – li – no, bel u – ce – li – no, Co – me
– no, U – ce – li – no, bel u – ce – li – no, Co – me
– no, U – ce – li – no, bel u – ce – li – no, Co – me

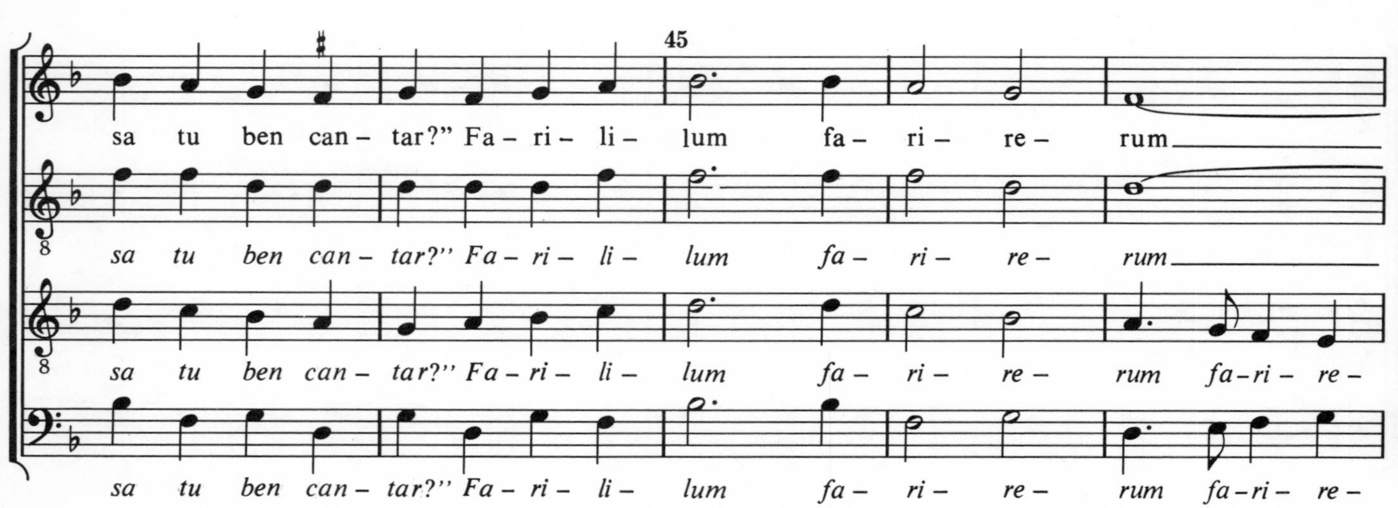
45
sa tu ben can – tar?" Fa – ri – li – lum fa – ri – re – rum
sa tu ben can – tar?" Fa – ri – li – lum fa – ri – re – rum
sa tu ben can – tar?" Fa – ri – li – lum fa – ri – re – rum fa – ri – re –
sa tu ben can – tar?" Fa – ri – li – lum fa – ri – re – rum fa – ri – re –

[16.] Ben mi credea passar

tem – po ho – ma – i Co –
pas – sar mio tem – – po ho-ma – i
tem – po ho – ma – i Co –
pas – sar mio tem – po ho – ma – i

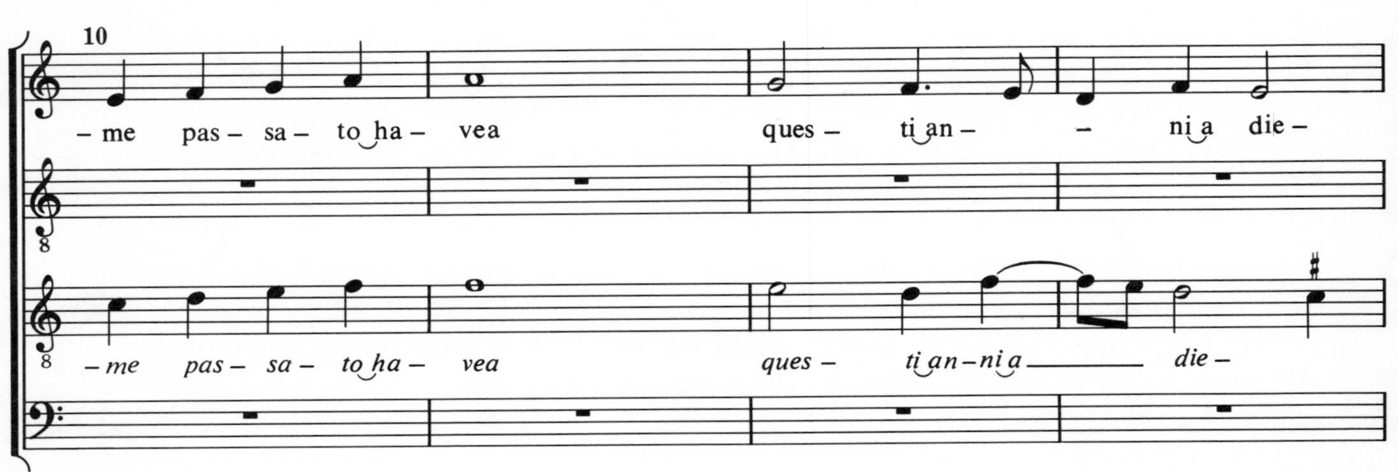
10
– me pas – sa – to ha – vea ques – ti an – – ni a die –
– me pas – sa – to ha – vea ques – ti an – ni a die –

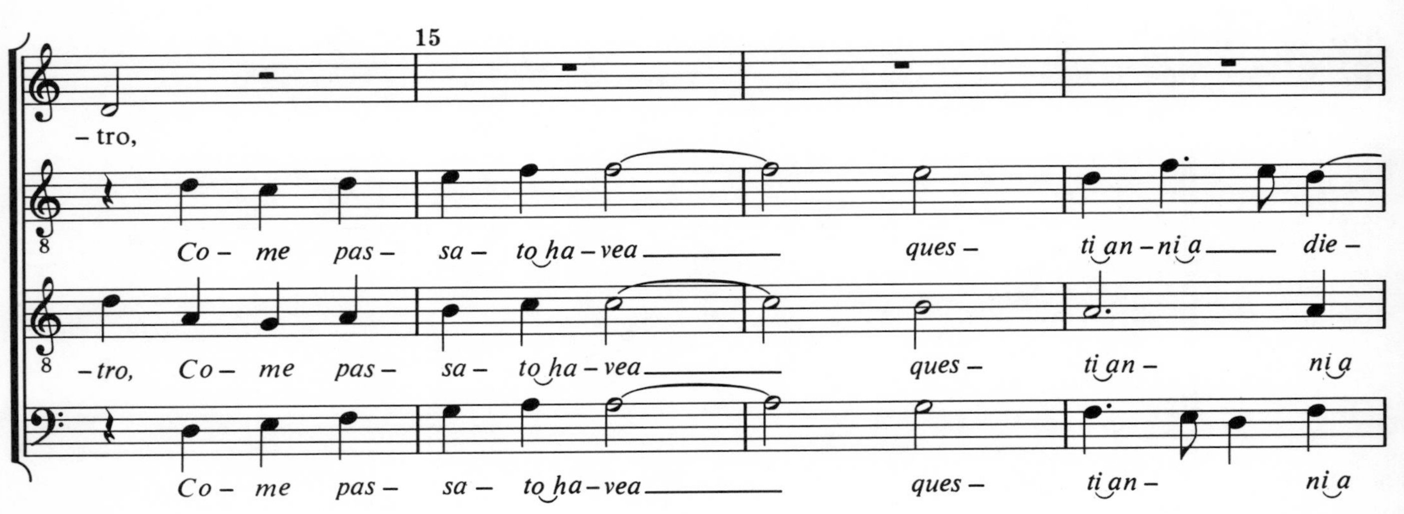
15
– tro,
Co – me pas – sa – to ha – vea ques – ti an – ni a die –
– tro, Co – me pas – sa – to ha – vea ques – ti an – ni a
Co – me pas – sa – to ha – vea ques – ti an – ni a

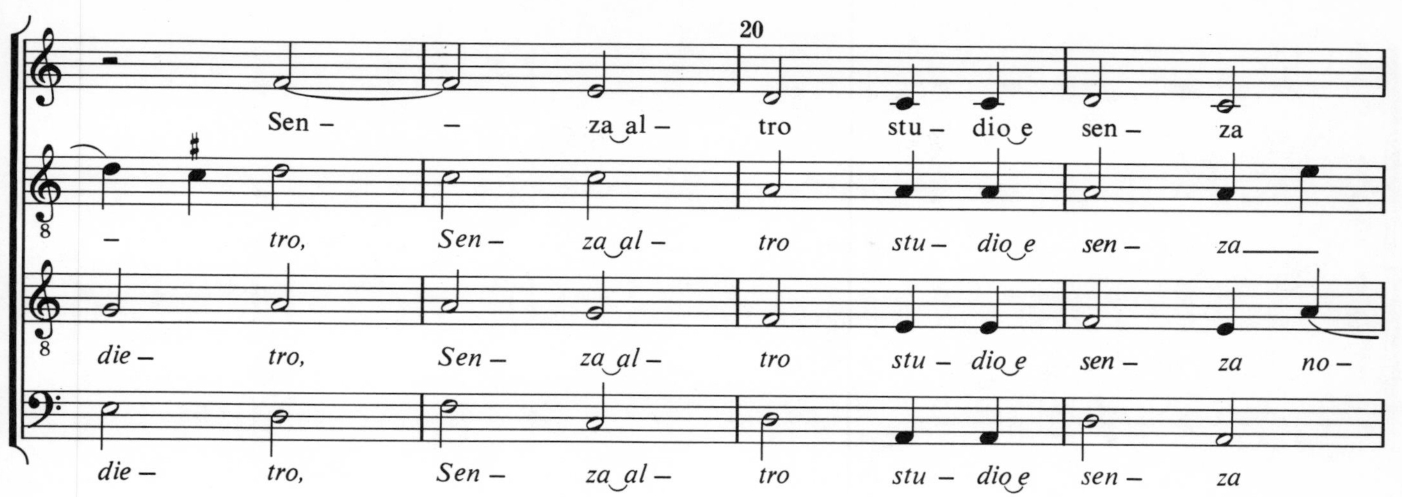
20
Sen – – za al – tro stu – dio e sen – za
– tro, Sen – za al – tro stu – dio e sen – za
die – tro, Sen – za al – tro stu – dio e sen – za no –
die – tro, Sen – za al – tro stu – dio e sen – za

25
no – vi in – ge – gni: Hor poi – chè da ma – don – na io non im –
no – vi in – ge – gni: Hor poi – chè da ma – don – na io non im –
– vi in – ge – gni: Hor poi – chè da ma – don – na io non im –
no – vi in – ge – gni: Hor poi – chè da ma – don – na io non im –

– pe – tro L'u – sa – – ta a – i – ta, a
– pe – tro L'u – sa – ta a – i – ta, a
– pe – tro L'u – sa – – ta a – i – ta, a
– pe – tro L'u – sa – ta a – i – ta, a

30
che con – dut – to m'ha – i. Tu'l ve – di, a – mor, che
che con – dut – to m'ha – i. Tu'l ve – di, a – mor, che
che con – dut – to m'ha – i. Tu'l ve – di, a – mor, che
che con – dut – to m'ha – i. Tu'l ve – di, a – mor, che

35
tal ar – te m'in – se – gni. Non so s'i' me
tal ar – te m'in – se – gni. Non so s'i' me
tal ar – te m'in – se – gni. Non so s'i' me
tal ar – te m'in – se – gni. Non so s'i' me

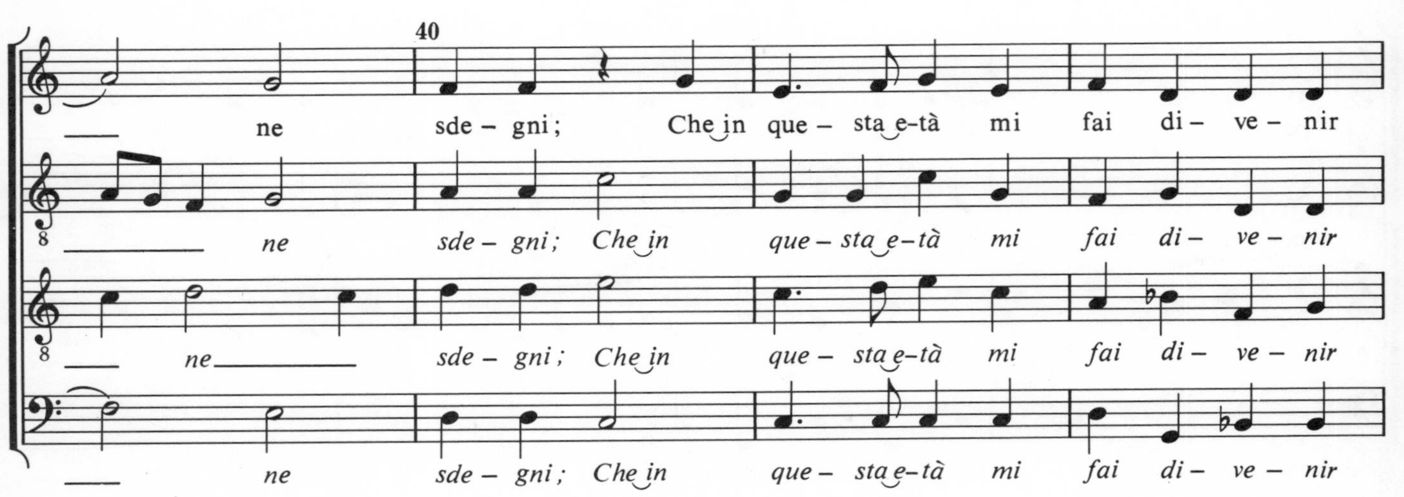
40
ne sde – gni; Che in que – sta e – tà mi fai di – ve – nir
ne sde – gni; Che in que – sta e – tà mi fai di – ve – nir
ne sde – gni; Che in que – sta e – tà mi fai di – ve – nir
ne sde – gni; Che in que – sta e – tà mi fai di – ve – nir

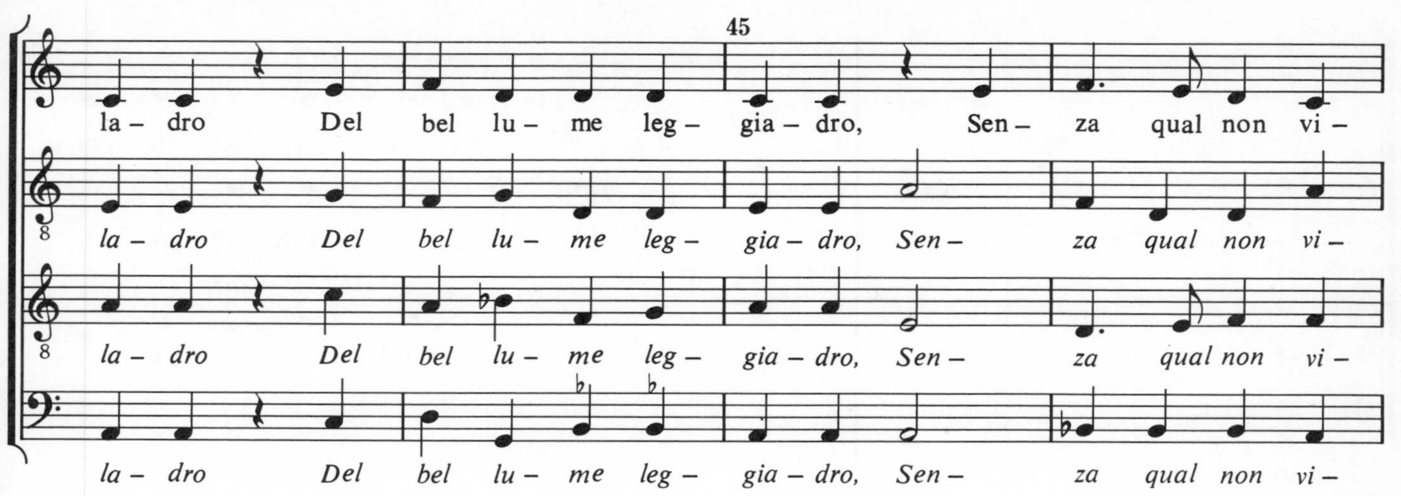
45
la – dro Del bel lu – me leg – gia – dro, Sen – za qual non vi –
la – dro Del bel lu – me leg – gia – dro, Sen – za qual non vi –
la – dro Del bel lu – me leg – gia – dro, Sen – za qual non vi –
la – dro Del bel lu – me leg – gia – dro, Sen – za qual non vi –

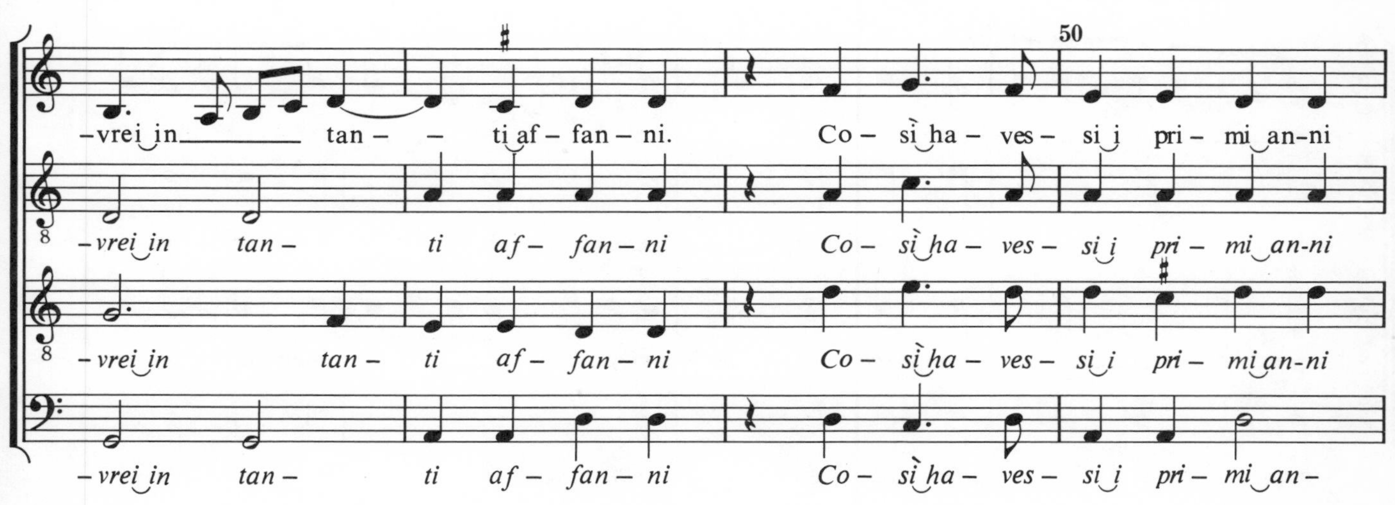
50
–vrei in tan – ti af – fan – ni. Co – sì ha – ves – si i pri – mi an-ni
–vrei in tan – ti af – fan – ni Co – sì ha – ves – si i pri – mi an-ni
–vrei in tan – ti af – fan – ni Co – sì ha – ves – si i pri – mi an-ni
–vrei in tan – ti af – fan – ni Co – sì ha – ves – si i pri – mi an –

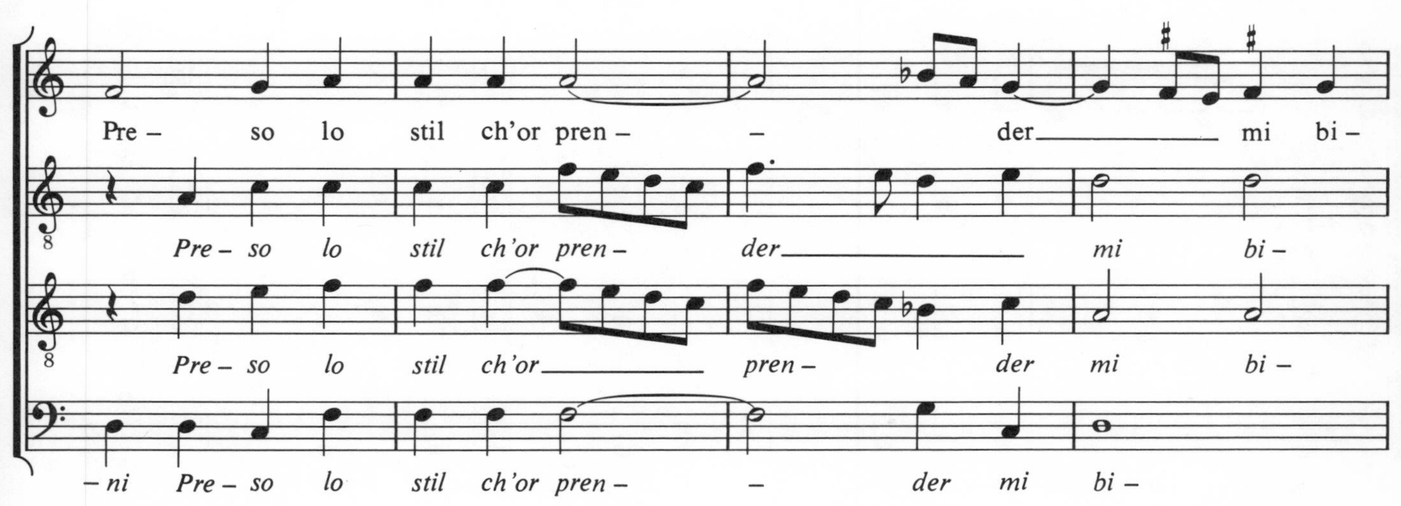
Pre – so lo stil ch'or pren – – der mi bi –
Pre – so lo stil ch'or pren – der mi bi –
Pre – so lo stil ch'or pren – der mi bi –
– ni Pre – so lo stil ch'or pren – – der mi bi –

55
– so – gna ; Che'n gio – ve – nil fal – li – re è men ver – go – gnia,
– so – gna; Che'n gio – ve – nil fal – li – re è men ver – go –
– so – gna ; Che'n gio – ve – nil fal – li – re è men ver – go –
– so – gna; Che'n gio – ve – nil fal – li – re è men ver – go –

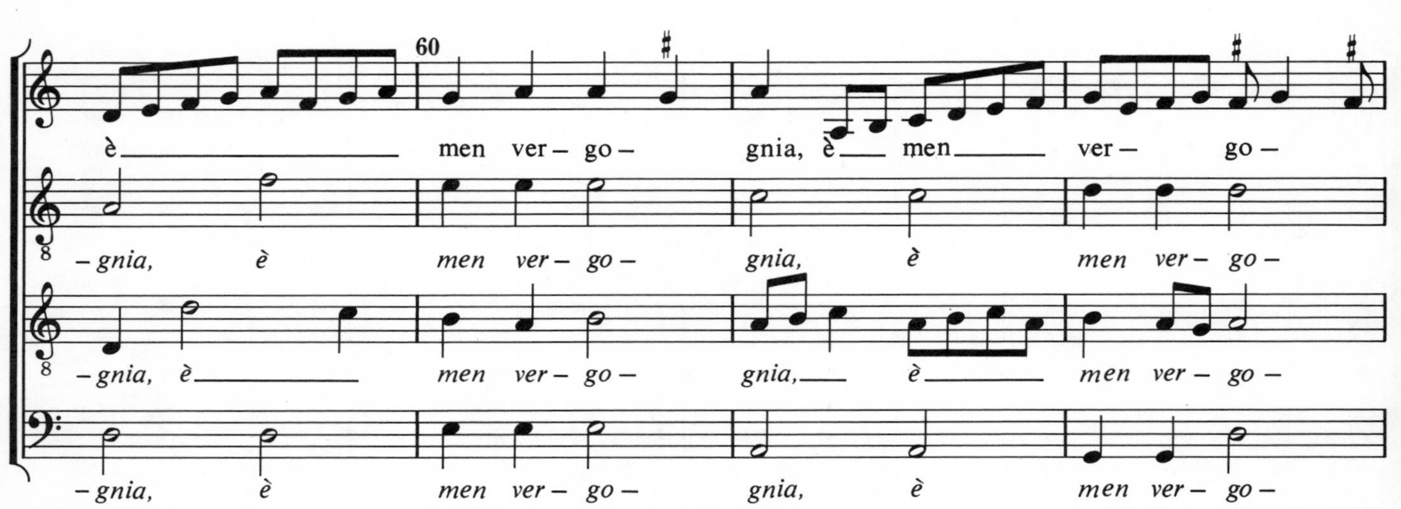
60
è men ver – go – gnia, è men ver – go –
– gnia, è men ver – go – gnia, è men ver – go –
– gnia, è men ver – go – gnia, è men ver – go –
– gnia, è men ver – go – gnia, è men ver – go –

65
– gnia, è men ver – go – gnia.
– gnia, ver – go – gnia, è men ver – go – gnia.
– gnia, ver – go – gnia, è men ver – go – gnia.
– gnia, ver – go – gnia, è men ver–go – gnia.

[17.] Come senza costei viver

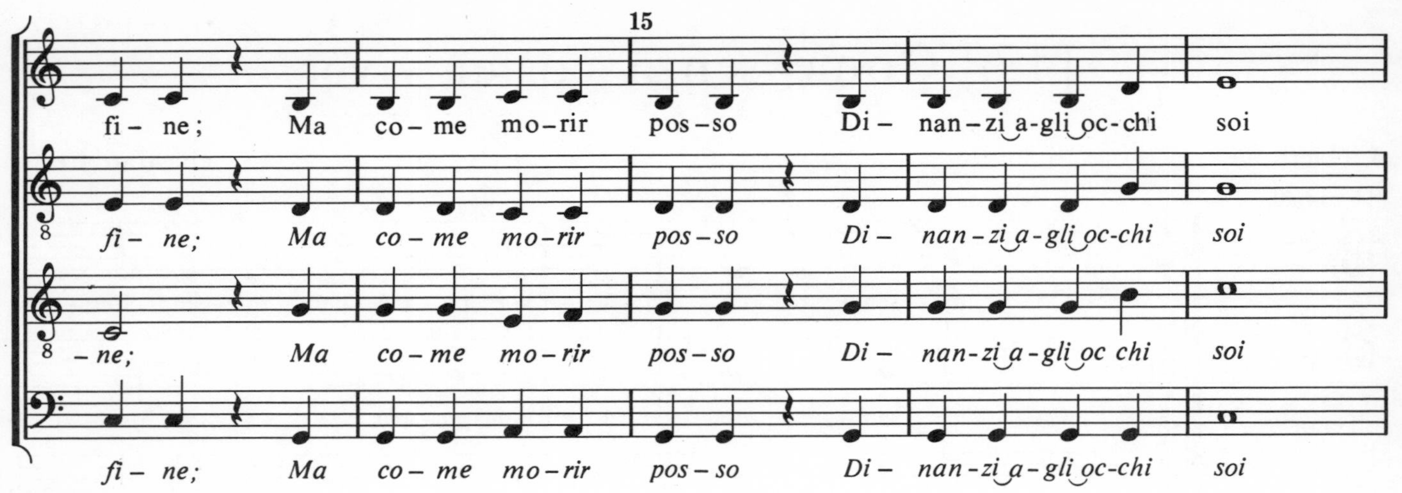
15
fi – ne ; Ma co – me mo – rir pos – so Di – nan – zi a - gli oc - chi soi
fi – ne; Ma co – me mo – rir pos – so Di – nan – zi a - gli oc - chi soi
– ne; Ma co – me mo – rir pos – so Di – nan – zi a - gli oc chi soi
fi – ne; Ma co – me mo – rir pos – so Di – nan – zi a - gli oc - chi soi

20
che son mia vi – ta? Hai – mè il sguar - do gen – til che m'ha per –
che son mia vi – ta? Hai – mè il sguar - do gen – til che m'ha per –
che son mia vi – ta? Hai – mè il sguar - do gen – til che m'ha per –
che son mia vi – ta? Hai – mè il sguar - do gen – til che m'ha per –

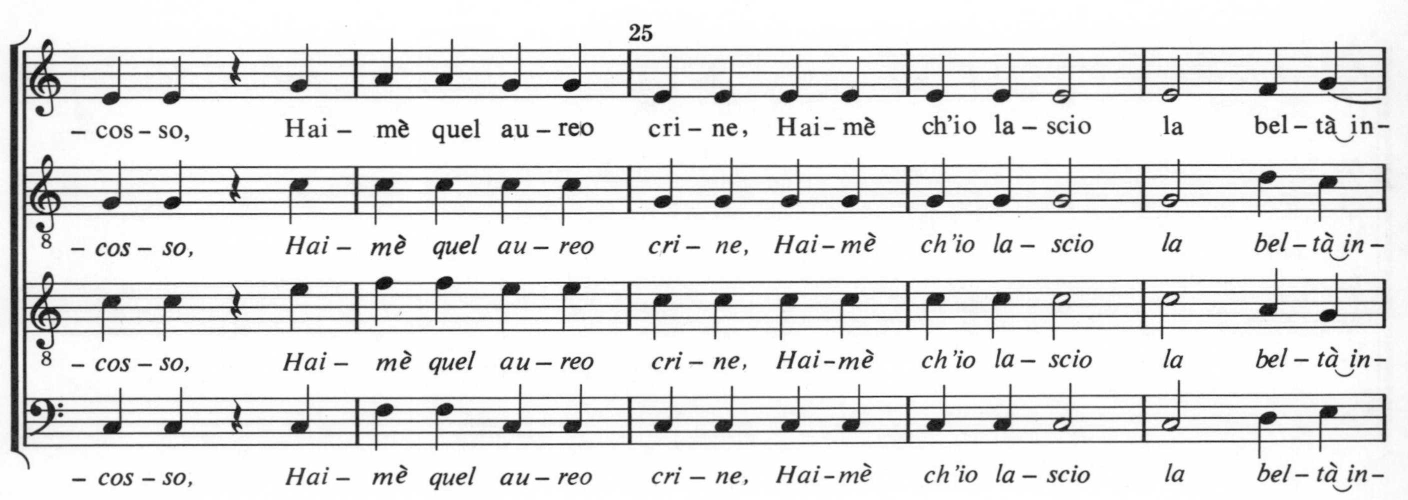
25
– cos – so, Hai – mè quel au – reo cri – ne, Hai - mè ch'io la – scio la bel – tà in –
– cos – so, Hai – mè quel au – reo cri – ne, Hai - mè ch'io la – scio la bel – tà in –
– cos – so, Hai – mè quel au – reo cri – ne, Hai - mè ch'io la – scio la bel – tà in –
– cos – so, Hai – mè quel au – reo cri – ne, Hai - mè ch'io la – scio la bel – tà in –

30
– fi – ni – ta, Ahi du – ra di – par – ti – ta! Qual cie – co me n'an –
– fi – ni – ta, Ahi du – ra di – par – ti – ta! Qual cie – co me n'an –
– fi – ni – ta, Ahi du – ra di – par – ti – ta! Qual cie – co me n'an –
– fi – ni – ta Ahi du – ra di – par – ti – ta! Qual cie – co me n'an –

35
– drò do – ve non lu – ce; Ma – don – na el mio mar –
– drò do – ve non lu – ce; Ma-don-na el mio mar—tir mi –
– drò do – ve non lu – ce; Ma – don – na el mio mar-tir
– drò do – ve non lu – ce; Ma – don – na el mio mar –

40
– tir mi – ser ad – du – – ce, mi – ser ad – du – ce.
– ser ad – – du – – ce, mi – ser ad – du – ce.
mi – ser ad – du – ce, mi – ser ad – du – ce.
– tir mi – – ser ad – du – ce.

[18.] E discalza e discalzetta

Anonymous

M[archetto] C[ara]

[19.] Alma gentil, che di tua vaga spoglia

Anonymous

M[archetto] C[ara]

5
di toi bei cos – tu – mi il mon – do or – na – sti, E al tuo par – tir in

10
pian – to mi la – scia – sti. So – lea con la bel –

15
– tà star – si ho ne – sta – te Al – la dol – ce om – bra di

20
toi chia – ri sguar-di, E den – tro al di – vin vol – to
Che'l ciel die – de et hor per se l'ha tol – to, E
25
cia – scun pa – rea dir la tua bel – ta – de,
la tua beltade
la tua beltade
la tua beltade

30
Mi – nor ve – drai si poi d'a – mor non ar –

35
– di, Ma pur la ca – sti – ta – de A – gli ho-ne – sti pen –

40
– sier sol da – va lo – co, On – de a – spet – ti a – gua –

45
-glian-do il ghiac- cio al fo- co. Tan-
8
8

50
-ti cuor fat- ti in- na- mo- ra- ti et ca- sti, Quan-te vol-
8
8

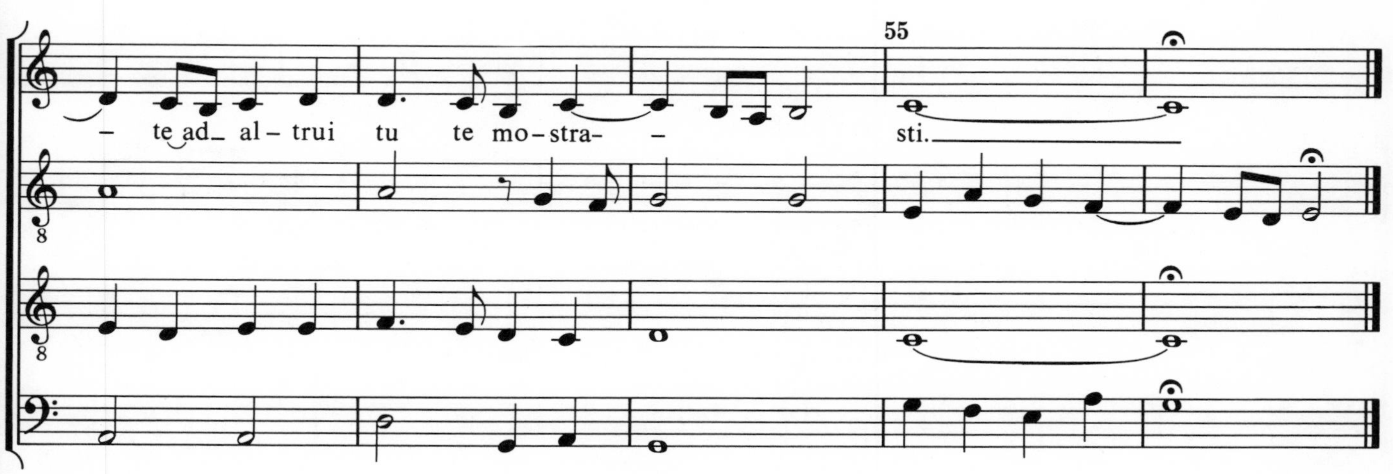
55
- te ad- al- trui tu te mo-stra- - sti.
8
8

[20.] Amor, che me tormenti

Anonymous

Sebastian Festa

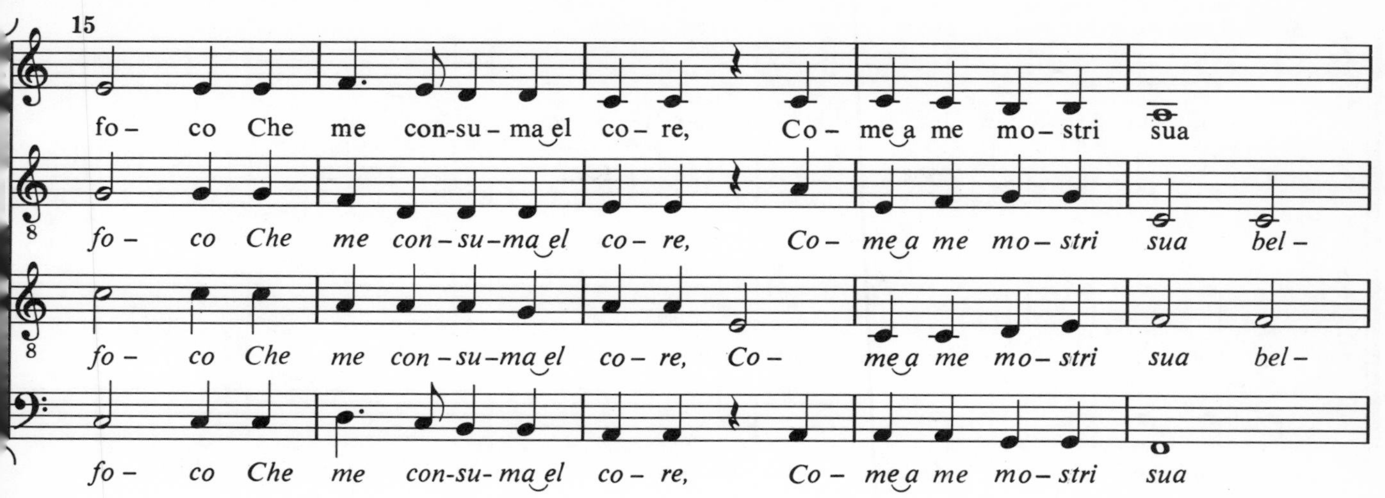
15
fo – co Che me con-su – ma el co – re, Co – me a me mo – stri sua
fo – co Che me con – su – ma el co – re, Co – me a me mo – stri sua bel –
fo – co Che me con – su – ma el co – re, Co – me a me mo – stri sua bel –
fo – co Che me con-su- ma el co – re, Co – me a me mo – stri sua

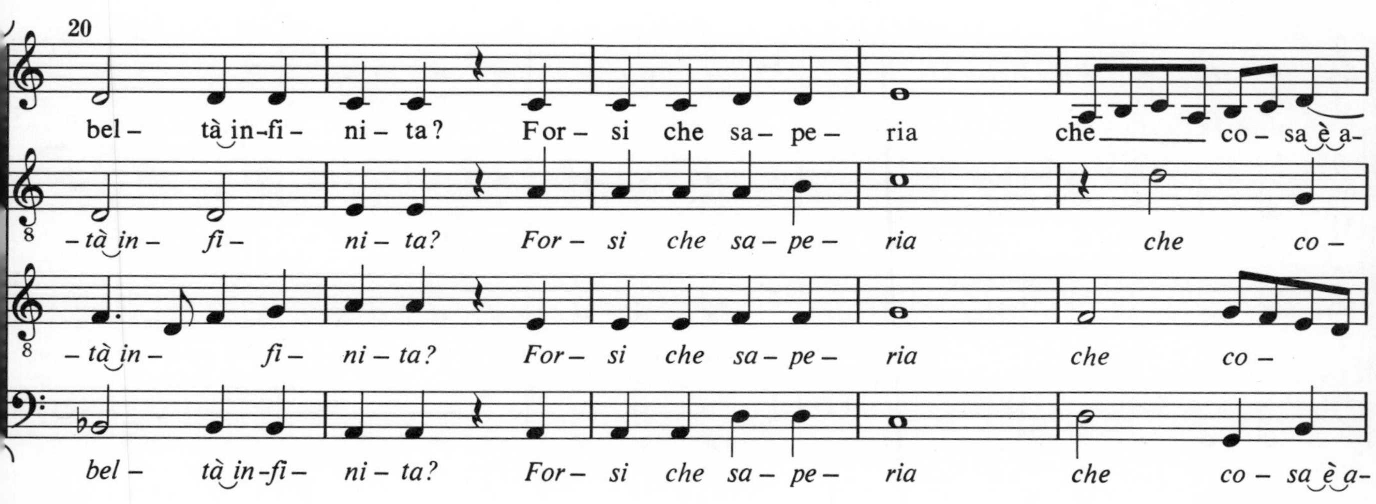
20
bel – tà in-fi – ni – ta? For – si che sa- pe – ria che co – sa è a-
– tà in – fi – ni – ta? For – si che sa – pe – ria che co –
– tà in – fi – ni – ta? For – si che sa – pe – ria che co –
bel – tà in-fi – ni – ta? For – si che sa – pe – ria che co – sa è a-

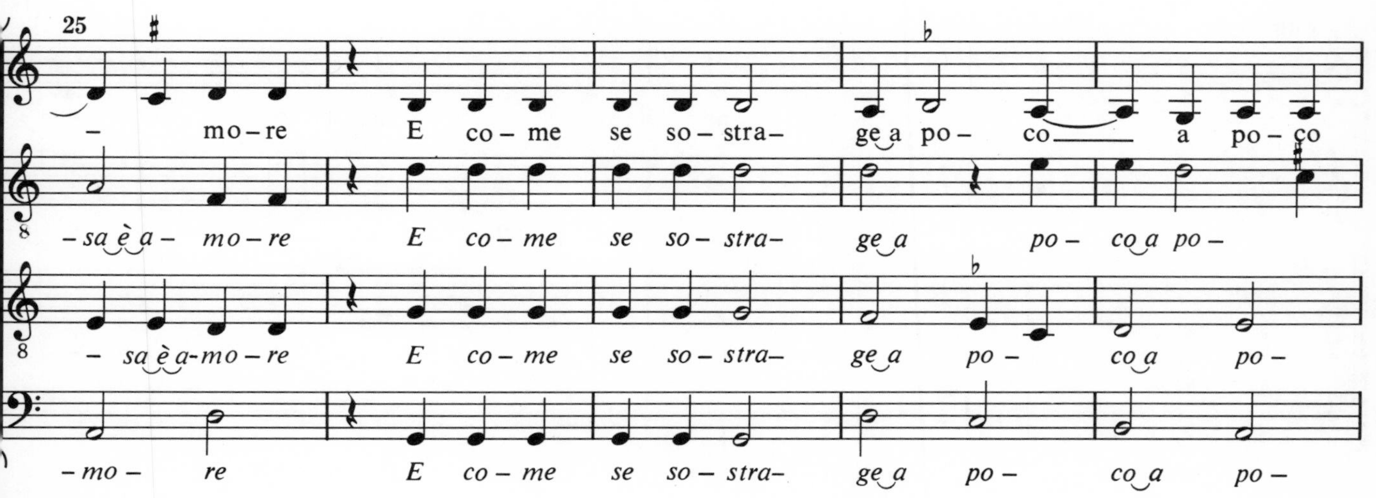
25
– mo – re E co – me se so – stra – ge a po – co a po – co
– sa è a – mo – re E co – me se so – stra – ge a po – co a po –
– sa è a-mo – re E co – me se so – stra – ge a po – co a po –
– mo – re E co – me se so – stra – ge a po – co a po –

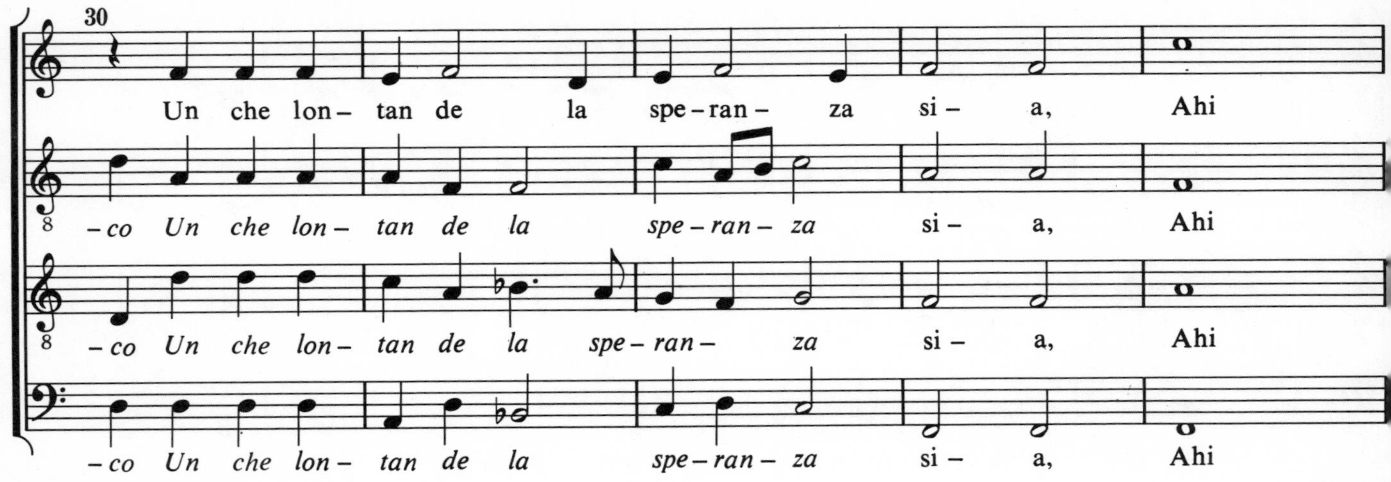
30
Un che lon– tan de la spe–ran– za si – a, Ahi
–co Un che lon– tan de la spe–ran– za si – a, Ahi
–co Un che lon– tan de la spe–ran– za si – a, Ahi
–co Un che lon– tan de la spe–ran– za si – a, Ahi

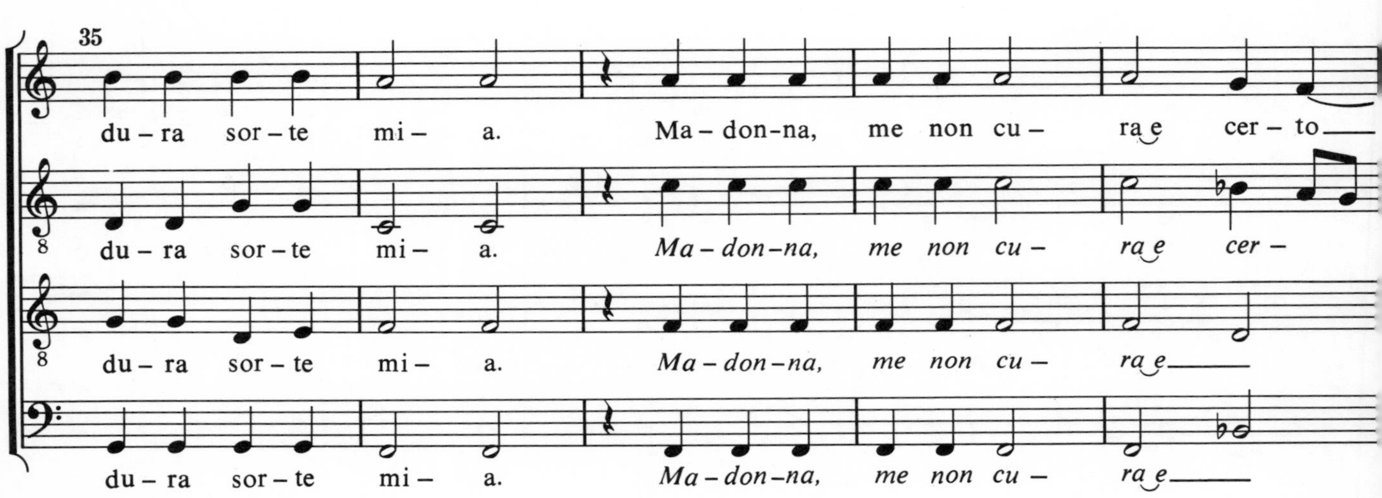
35
du – ra sor – te mi – a. Ma – don–na, me non cu – ra e cer – to
du – ra sor–te mi – a. Ma – don–na, me non cu – ra e cer –
du – ra sor – te mi – a. Ma – don – na, me non cu – ra e
du – ra sor – te mi – a. Ma – don – na, me non cu – ra e

40
ve – de Che al–tro non re – gna in me, che a-
– to ve – de Che al–tro non re – gna in me, che a-
cer – to ve – de Che al–tro non re – gna in me, che a –
cer – to ve – de Che al–tro non re – gna in me, che a –

45
– – – mor e fe –
–mor e fe – – de, Che al-tro non re – gna,
– mor, a – mor e fe – de,
– mor, a – – mor e fe – – de,

50
– de, Che al-tro non re – – gna in me, che a – –
Che al-tro non re-gna in me, che a-mor e fe –
Che al-tro non re – gna in me, che a – mor,
Che al-tro non re – – gna in me, che a – mor, a –

55
– – mor e fe – de, a – mor e fe – de.
– de, che a– mor e fe – de, che a– mor e fe – de.
a – mor e fe – de, che a-mor e fe – de.
– mor e fe – de, che a-mor e fe – de.

[21.] L'ultimo dì de maggio

Anonymous

Sebastian Festa

15
–com–pa– gna– – ta;
–com–pa– gna– – ta;
–le ac–com– pa– gna– – ta; O– gni u-na in– na– mo– ra– ta,
–com–pa– gna– – ta; O– gni u-na in– na– mo– ra– ta,

20
Gen— til, ac– cor– ta e bel– la. Tan– da–ri– don–
Gen– til, ac– cor– ta e bel– la. Tan– da–ri– don–
Gen– til, ac– cor– ta e bel– la. Tan– da–ri– don–
Gen– til, ac– cor– ta e bel– la. Tan– da–ri– don–

25
–del–la, Tan– da– ri– don-del– – la. Oi– mè, che l'è pur quel-la
–del–la, Tan– da– ri– don– del– la. Oi– mè, che l'è pur quel–la
–del–la, Tan– da– ri– don– del– la.
–del–la, Tan– da– ri– don– del– la.

Che m'ha li – ga – to il cor, che me l'ha tol – to Con
Che m'ha li – – ga – to il cor, che me l'ha tol – to Con
Che m'ha li – ga – to il cor, che me l'ha tol – to Con
Che m'ha li – ga – to il cor, che me l'ha tol – to Con

la bel – tà del suo splen – den – te vol – to.
la bel – tà del suo splen – den – te vol – to, Con
la bel – tà del suo splen – den – te vol – to, Con
la bel – tà del suo splen – den – te vol – to, Con

la bel – tà del suo splen–den – te vol – to.
la bel – tà del suo splen–den – te vol – to.
la bel – tà del suo splen–den – te vol – to.

[22.] E dapoi che'l sol dal monte

ALVERNO COLLEGE LIBRARY
Libro primo de la croce
FAL 782.43 L697